HYMNS

for worship

CALVIN INSTITUTE OF CHRISTIAN WORSHIP
for the study and renewal of worship

FAITH
ALIVE®
Christian Resources

Calvin Institute of Christian Worship
Grand Rapids, Michigan 49546

Faith Alive Christian Resources
Grand Rapids, Michigan 49560

Hymns for Worship is copublished by:

The Calvin Institute of Christian Worship, 1855 Knollcrest Circle SE, Grand
Rapids, MI 49546; phone: 616-526-6088; fax: 616-526-7168; e-mail: worship@
calvin.edu; website: www.calvin.edu/worship.

and

Faith Alive Christian Resources, 2850 Kalamazoo Ave. SE, Grand Rapids,
MI 49560; phone: 800-333-8300; e-mail: info@faithaliveresources.org;
website: www.FaithAliveResources.org.

ISBN 978-1-59255-443-0 Regular Binding
ISBN 978-1-59255-519-2 Spiral Binding

10 9 8 7 6 5 4 3 2 1

Mixed Sources
Product group from well-managed
forests and other controlled sources
www.fsc.org Cert no. SW-COC-002283
© 1996 Forest Stewardship Council
FSC

Contents

Preface

You are holding an unusual hymnal! The texts here are not grouped by theme, season of the year, or order of worship. Rather, they are presented in chronological order by *text*, beginning with a sampling of Old Testament psalms and continuing right up to songs written in the past few years. Paging through this book, then, is like taking a 3000 year journey through the songs of God's people.

This volume is part of a series of song collections co-published by the Calvin Institute of Christian Worship and Faith Alive Christian Resources. It is our hope that this particular collection will be useful in the Christian community in at least the following ways:

- as an ecumenical source to access the rich heritage of Christian hymns for congregations who wish to supplement their own tradition of hymnody.
- as a compact collection of great hymns to sing during their personal, family, or small group devotions.
- as a supplement to the academic study of church history, historical and systematic theology, pastoral ministry, and hymnology.
- as a vehicle for the Christian Reformed Church in North America and the Reformed Church in America to dialogue about which hymns should be part of their forthcoming bi-denominational hymnal. This anthology may also be a useful resource for other hymnal committees when they consider which classic hymns bind Christians together across denominational lines.

This collection was formulated by examining various lists of "core" hymnody. Such lists are based, in part, on descriptive statistical tabulations of which hymns appear most often in recent North American and British English-language hymnals for Roman Catholics and Protestants. The lists are also based on prescriptive suggestions from hymnologists and theologians about which are the "great" hymns of the Christian tradition, even if they're not always the most popular ones.

This anthology includes a rich variety of hymn tunes: those that are based on plainchant, folk melodies, historic psalm tunes, and musical settings uniquely composed for a specific text, as well as hymn tunes drawn from a large variety of classic and contemporary hymnals published for Protestant and Roman Catholic use.

One of the most fascinating aspects of hymnody is how a specific text and its tune are "wed," as in many cases a hymn text may appear in different hymnals with a variety of tunes. Yet it is also the case that certain texts are inseparably paired with certain tunes, such as happened to a number of hymns first published in important British collections such as *Hymns Ancient and Modern* or the *English Hymnal*. Virtually every Christian sings "Holy, Holy,

Holy, Lord God Almighty" to the NICAEA tune, but there is less consensus on which tune belongs to "When I Survey the Wondrous Cross." This collection offers the union of texts and tunes that are most common in North America for most hymns, but there may be some surprises or novel matches.

Finding Your Way

The Order

As previously mentioned, this hymnal is organized in chronological order, beginning with settings of a few Old Testament psalm texts and New Testament canticles, so as not to divorce them completely from the heritage of hymnody. Then follows early and medieval Christian hymnody, hymns from the Protestant Reformation, from the great hymn authors of the eighteenth and nineteenth centuries in England, and from mostly nineteenth-century sources in the United States. The collection ends with two groups of English-language hymns from the twentieth century; the most contemporary text in this hymnal dates from 2006. Words or music credits followed by P.D. are in the public domain.

It was our thought that printing these hymns in chronological sequence would help identify the historical development of Christian hymnody over some three thousand years. An index in the back of this collection provides ready access to its contents in alphabetical order.

Song Titles

For those not well-versed in hymnological details, we offer the following explanations. Hymn-text titles are usually drawn from the opening line of text, or sometimes from a key phrase in a refrain. In the latter case we provide both titles on the page and in the index. As is customary, the author or source of each text is identified, as is the composer, arranger, or source for the tune in each case. Our additional notes give extra details for each hymn, offering a glimpse of its historical or performance context. Full commentary on the textual and musical history of each hymn can be found in a variety of hymnal handbooks or companions and increasingly on www.hymnary.org.

The Meter

What is less well-known is that hymn texts, like traditional poetry, have historically been written in meter—that is, with fixed patterns of phrase lengths and accents. Thus each hymn has a mathematical identifier. For example, "88 88" means each stanza of that hymn has four lines and each line contains eight syllables. "8787 D" means there are alternating lines of eight and seven syllables in an eight-line or double stanza.

What these mathematical descriptors do not tell, however, is the accent pattern. Many hymn texts have a metrical pattern that is either trochaic (a series of strong/weak accents) or iambic (a series of weak/strong accents). There are other more complicated patterns, and sometimes a hymn is inconsistent in its phrase lengths or accents. Thus a text that has 86 86 phrase lengths could be sung to various tunes that correspond to this 86 86 structure;

however, the accent pattern of the text must always correspond to the accent pattern of the music. A metrical index is provided in the back of this hymnal.

Hymn texts almost always exhibit rhyme; this enables and promotes memorization. Rhyming patterns such as abab, abcb, and aabb are commonly found. One reason "great" hymns attain their classic status and merit continuing inclusion in modern hymnals is their incorporation of direct biblical phrases and/or allusions to biblical text into the language of the hymn. This collection of hymns is accompanied by an online biblical index and a topical index available at www.hymnary.org.

Tune Names

Hymn tunes are named, and by convention their names are spelled in uppercase letters. For example, "ST. ANNE" is the name of the tune associated with the text "O God, Our Help in Ages Past." Hymn tune names often bear some historical significance, but are sometimes assigned quite arbitrarily or mysteriously, it seems, by either the composer or a hymnal editor. There is a hymn tune index in the back of this collection, and there is a chronological index of hymn tunes online.

Song Notes

Song notes for each hymn are found at the end of the song and are included to suggest something of their literary, theological, musical, and pastoral importance. There are even a few hymns in this collection that merit inclusion for their historical significance or popularity, but which fail the test of "greatness" in the judgment of the compilers and deserve critical commentary.

Acknowledgements

We want to express our debt to C. Michael Hawn and Peter W. Cutts, who independently formulated lists of "core" Christian hymnody for the journal *The Hymn* and the revision of Erik Routley's *An English-Speaking Hymnal Guide,* respectively. Their tabulations were supplemented and updated by student staff at the Calvin Institute of Christian Worship, and then reviewed by a group of hymnologists during a seminar at Calvin College on the "Teaching of Hymnology."

We extend our profound gratitude to three staff members of the Calvin Institute of Christian Worship for joining us in various meetings to establish the final contents of this volume: Emily Brink, Bethany Vrieland, and John Witvliet. We also thank Cindy DeBoer for copyright work.

We are grateful to Faith Alive Christian Resources staff members Diane Dykgraaf, Rachel Katje, Lynn Setsma, Sandy Swartzentruber, and Kyle Thompson for their editorial, administrative, and copyright support.

Bert Polman, editor
Calvin Institute of Christian Worship

Joyce Borger, series editor
Faith Alive Christian Resources

Psalm 13: How Long, LORD?   1a

1. How long, LORD? Will you forget | me forever? *
    How long will you hide your | face from me?
2. How long must I wrestle with my thoughts
    and day after day have sorrow | in my heart? *
    How long will my enemy triumph | over me?   R
3. Look on me and answer, | LORD my God. *
    Give light to my eyes, or I will | sleep in death,
4. and my enemy will say, "I have | overcome him," *
    and my foes will rejoice | when I fail.   R
5. But I trust in your un- | failing love; *
    my heart rejoices in | your salvation.
6. I will sing the | LORD's praise, *
    for he has been | good to me.   R

Glory be to the Father and | to the Son *
    and to the | Holy Spirit;
as it was in the beginning, | is now,*
    and will be forever. | Amen.   R

Words: Psalm 13 (TNIV) and "Glory be …" TNIV © 2001, 2005 by International Bible Society®
Music: Richard W. Hillert © 1978 *Lutheran Book of Worship*

The chanting of psalms is an important practice in Christian worship, and this example comes from contemporary Lutheranism. This setting is a plainsong formula which is repeated for each two verses of text, making it a
"double" chant. The psalm is "pointed" for singing, with an asterisk indicating the division of each verse into two
portions. Most of the text of each portion is sung to the reciting tone (the double whole note), and the vertical line
indicates the start of the cadential tones. Ordinarily there is one syllable of text for each cadential tone; when there
are only two syllables, the first syllable is sung to two tones. Sing this in speech rhythm, not in equal quarter notes.

1b   Psalm 13: How Long, LORD?

Vs. 1-4

Vs. 5-6 and Gloria

1. How long, O LORD? Will you forget | me for- | ever? *
   How long will you | hide your | face from | me?
2. How long must I bear pain in my soul,
       and have sorrow in my heart | all day | long? *
   How long shall my enemy be ex- | alted | over | me?   R
3. Consider and answer me, O | LORD my | God! *
   Give light to my eyes, or I will | sleep the | sleep of | death,
4. and my enemy will say, "I | have pre- | vailed"; *
   my foes will rejoice be- | cause I | am | shaken.   R
5. But I trusted in your | steadfast | love; *
   my heart shall re- | joice in | your sal- | vation.
6. I will sing | to the | LORD, *
   because he has dealt bounti- | fully | with | me.   R

Glory be to the Father and to the Son and to the | Holy | Spirit; *
as it was in the beginning, is now, and will be for- | ever. | A- | men.   R

Words: Psalm 13 (NRSV) and "Glory be…" NRSV © 1989 by the Division of Christian Education of National
    Council of the Churches of Christ in the USA.
Music: Philip Hayes (1738-1797), P.D.

This is an example of an Anglican psalm chant, intended for singing in harmony. It is a "single" chant, repeated
for each verse of the text. But note that the music in minor is used for stanzas 1-4 and the music in major is used
for stanzas 5-6 and the "Glory be …" Please observe the difference in "pointing" for this chant, as the cadential
formula for the second part of each verse is longer here than in the Lutheran example. Again, sing this in textual
rhythm, not in equal quarter notes.

Psalm 13: How Long, Lord?   1c

Be still, my soul, the Lord is on your side. Lord is on your side.

Refrain

1. How long, Lord? Will you forget me forever?
   How long will you hide your face from me?
2. How long must I wrestle with my thoughts
   and day after day have sorrow in my heart?
   How long will my enemy triumph over me?

Refrain

3. Look on me and answer, Lord my God.
   Give light to my eyes, or I will sleep in death,
4. and my enemy will say, "I have overcome him,"
   and my foes will rejoice when I fail.

Refrain

5. But I trust in your unfailing love;
   my heart rejoices in your salvation.
6. I will sing the Lord's praise,
   for he has been good to me.

Refrain

Glory be to the Father and to the Son and to the Holy Spirit;
as it was in the beginning, is now, and will be forever. Amen.

Refrain

Words: Katharina A. von Schlegel (1752); tr. Jane L. Borthwick (1855) alt., P.D.
Music: Jean Sibelius (1900); arr. © *Presbyterian Hymnal* (1933)
Scripture text: Psalm 13 (TNIV) (and "Glory be . . . " TNIV)© 2001, 2005 by International Bible Society®

One of the modern practices of psalmody is reading a psalm text and singing an appropriate refrain. You could choose either of the translations of this psalm for unison reading (1b or 1c) and then sing the refrain at the R mark (use the second ending of the refrain after "Glory be …").

2 Psalm 23:
The Lord's My Shepherd, I'll Not Want

1 The Lord's my Shepherd, I'll not want.
2 My soul he doth restore again;
3 Yea, though I walk in death's dark vale,
4 My table thou hast furnished

He makes me down to lie in pastures green;
and me to walk doth make within the paths
yet will I fear no ill; for thou art with
in presence of my foes; my head thou dost

he leadeth me the quiet waters by.
of righteousness, e'en for his own name's sake.
me, and thy rod and staff me comfort still.
with oil anoint, and my cup overflows.

5 Goodness and mercy all my life
shall surely follow me;
and in God's house forevermore
my dwelling place shall be.

Words: Psalm 23; vers. Scottish Psalter (1650), P.D.
Music: Jessie S. Irvine (1872); harm. David Grant (1872), P.D.

86 86
CRIMOND

Psalm 23 is the oft-memorized psalm of trust that has comforted Jews and Christians for centuries. The traditional versification offered here is from the Scottish *Psalms of David in Meter* (1650), which, regardless of its mismatch of textual and musical phrases in stanza 1, was canonized by its union with CRIMOND at Queen Elizabeth's wedding to Prince Philip in 1947.

Psalm 84: How Lovely, Lord, How Lovely 3

1 How love - ly, Lord, how love - ly is your a - bid - ing place;
2 In your blest courts to wor - ship, O God, a sin - gle day
3 A sun and shield for - ev - er are you, O Lord most high;

my soul is long-ing, faint - ing, to feast up - on your grace.
is bet - ter than a thou - sand if I from you should stray;
you show - er us with bless - ings; no good will you de - ny.

The spar - row finds a shel - ter, a place to build her nest;
I'd rath - er keep the en - trance and claim you as my Lord
The saints, your grace re - ceiv - ing, from strength to strength shall go,

and so your tem - ple calls us with - in its walls to rest.
than rev - el in the rich - es the ways of sin af - ford.
and from their life shall riv - ers of bless - ing o - ver - flow.

Words: Arlo D. Duba (1980) © 1986 Hope Publishing Company.
Music: Hal H. Hopson © 1983 Hope Publishing Company.

76 76 D
MERLE'S MUSIC

This is one of the psalms of Zion in which the psalmist yearns for communion with God in his temple. A spoken New Testament interpretation that focuses on God's people as his temple might well precede the singing of this Old Testament confession of faith. The union of the textual précis by Duba with Hopson's gentle tune resulted from their common work on the Presbyterian Psalter Task Force.

(In order to avoid page turns this psalm appears before Psalm 72.)

4 Psalm 72: Hail to the Lord's Anointed

1 Hail to the Lord's a - noint - ed, great Da - vid's great - er son!
2 He shall come down like show - ers up - on the fruit - ful earth;
3 The des - ert tribes a - dore him and bend to him the knee;

Hail, in the time ap - point - ed, his reign on earth be - gun!
and love, joy, hope, like flow - ers, spring in his path to birth.
the wick - ed bow be - fore him, his glo - ry they will see.

He comes to break op - pres - sion, to set the cap - tive free,
The king shall have do - min - ion from sea to shin - ing sea,
With gifts of ad - o - ra - tion the for - eign kings shall meet

to take a - way trans - gres - sion, and rule in eq - ui - ty.
and o - ver ev - ery na - tion his peace-ful rule shall be.
to pour the wealth of na - tions in trib - ute at his feet.

Words: Psalm 72; vers. James Montgomery (1822); rev. Bert Polman (1985) © 1987 Faith Alive
  Christian Resources
Music: German folk melody, Memmingen (1610), P.D.

76 76 D
ES FLOG EIN KLEINS WALDVOGLEIN

4 He comes with rescue speedy to those who suffer wrong,
   to help the poor and needy, and bid the weak be strong.
   He turns their sighs to singing, their darkness into light,
   for they, condemned and dying, are precious in his sight.

5 His kingdom is increasing, a kingdom without end.
   For him shall prayer unceasing and daily praise ascend.
   The mountain dews will nourish a harvest from the fields;
   the grain and fruit will flourish, the land its bounty yields.

6 In name forever glorious, he on his throne shall rest,
   from age to age victorious, all blessing and all-blest.
   Praise God, who rules each nation; tell of his deeds again.
   His glory fills creation; sing praise to God. Amen!

Originally probably a coronation psalm, Psalm 72 has become a great text about the righteous and glorious reign of the Messiah, the Christ. Montgomery's loose paraphrase has been revised to bring it closer to the biblical text. The traditional folk melody has been revived in the twentieth century and used as a hymn tune since George R. Woodward's *Songs of Syon* (1910).

(In order to avoid page turns this psalm appears after Psalm 84.)

5   Psalm 98: Sing a New Song to the Lord

1 Sing a new song to the Lord, he to whom won-ders be-long!
2 Now to the ends of the earth see his sal-va-tion is shown!
3 Sing a new song and re-joice, pub-lish his prais-es a-broad!
4 Join with the hills and the sea, thun-ders of praise to pro-long!

Re-joice in his tri-umph and tell of his power—
And still he re-mem-bers his mer-cy and truth,
Let voic-es in cho-rus with trum-pet and horn,
In judg-ment and jus-tice he comes to the earth—

O sing to the Lord a new song!
un-chang-ing in love to his own.
re-sound for the joy of the Lord!
O sing to the Lord a new song!

Words: Timothy Dudley-Smith (1971) © 1973 Hope Publishing Company.
Music: David G. Wilson (1971), © 1973 Jubilate Hymns, Ltd. Hope Publishing Company

7 7 11 8
ONSLOW SQUARE

Psalm 98 is one of the great festival psalms in the Old Testament. It is cosmic in scope, exalting the Lord of justice with voices, instruments, and all creation. The command to "sing a new song" is here answered with a fine new tune for these words.

Psalm 100:   6
All People That on Earth Do Dwell

1 All people that on earth do dwell,
2 Know that the Lord is God indeed;
3 O enter then his gates with praise,
4 For why? The Lord our God is good,

sing to the Lord with cheerful voice;
without our aid he did us make.
approach with joy his courts unto;
his mercy is forever sure;

him serve with joy, his praise forth tell.
We are his folk, he doth us feed,
praise, laud, and bless his name always,
his truth at all times firmly stood,

Come ye before him and rejoice.
and for his sheep he doth us take.
for it is seemly so to do.
and shall from age to age endure.

Words: Psalm 100; vers. William Kethe (1561), alt., P.D.
Music: Louis Bourgeois, P.D.

88 88
OLD 100TH

Psalm 100 is the Hebrew equivalent of a cheerleader's shout. It encourages us to worship the Lord with joyful song because in his faithfulness he makes us his people. Kethe's paraphrase comes from the *Anglo-Genevan Psalter* (1561), which used the Genevan tune of Psalm 134 for Kethe's Psalm 100—hence the tune title.

7 Psalm 103:
Praise, My Soul, the King of Heaven

1 Praise, my soul, the King of heav - en; to his feet your
2 Praise him for his grace and fa - vor to his peo - ple
3 Fa - ther - like he tends and spares us; well our fee - ble
4 An - gels, help us to a - dore him; you be - hold him

trib - ute bring. Ran - somed, healed, re - stored, for - giv - en,
in dis - tress; praise him, still the same as ev - er,
frame he knows. In his hand he gent - ly bears us;
face to face. Sun and moon bow down be - fore him,

ev - er - more his prais - es sing: Al - le - lu - ia,
slow to chide, and swift to bless: Al - le - lu - ia,
res - cues us from all our foes. Al - le - lu - ia,
all who dwell in time and space. Al - le - lu - ia,

al - le - lu - ia! Praise the ev - er - last - ing King!
al - le - lu - ia! Glo - rious in his faith - ful - ness!
al - le - lu - ia! Wide - ly yet his mer - cy flows!
al - le - lu - ia! Praise with us the God of grace!

Words: Psalm 103; précis, Henry F. Lyte (1834), P.D.
Music: John Goss (1869), P.D.

87 87 87
LAUDA ANIMA

A minister in the Church of England, Lyte wrote numerous poems and hymns. This text is his summary of Psalm 103, minus the original fourth stanza. Goss composed this tune for Lyte's text and provided various harmonizations, which some modern hymnals include. It is rightly considered to be one of the finest hymns from nineteenth-century England.

Psalm 112: 8
How Blest Are Those Who Fear the LORD

1 How blest are those who fear the LORD and great-ly
2 A-bound-ing wealth shall bless their home, their right-eous-
3 The peo-ple who be-friend the weak in jus-tice
4 By e-vil tid-ings not dis-mayed, the right-eous

love God's ho-ly will. Their chil-dren share their
ness for-e'er en-dure. To them shall light a-
shall their cause main-tain. True peace shall their whole
trust in God a-lone. Their heart is stead-fast,

great re-ward, and bless-ings all their days shall fill.
rise in gloom, for they are mer-ci-ful and pure.
life at-tend, and long their mem-ory shall re-main.
un-a-fraid, for they shall see their foes o'er-thrown.

5 Dispersing gifts among the poor,
the righteous for their needs provide.
Their righteousness shall thus endure;
their strength in honor shall abide.

6 The wicked will be brought to shame,
while righteous ones will see the LORD.
Unrighteous hopes will not see gain,
for sin will find its due reward.

Words: Psalm 112; vers. *Psalter* (1887); rev. *Psalter Hymnal* (1987), © Faith Alive Christian Resources
Music: Samuel Webbe, Sr. (1782), P.D.

88 88
MELCOMBE

Psalm 112 is a wisdom psalm that contrasts the blessedness of the righteous with the damnation of the wicked. Webbe's tune was first published for Roman Catholic use, but quickly appeared in Protestant hymnals. It gained much popularity through inclusion in both *Hymns Ancient and Modern* (1861) and the *English Hymnal* (1906).

9 Psalm 116:
I Love the LORD, for He Has Heard My Voice

1 I love the LORD, for he has heard my voice.
2 Our God is gra - cious, mer - ci - ful, and just.
3 For you, O LORD, have saved my soul from death.
4 How can I pay the LORD for all his gifts?
5 Pre - cious to God the dy - ing of his saints.

He turned to me and heard my cry for mer - cy.
He watch - es o - ver all the sim - ple - heart - ed.
You kept my eyes from tears, my feet from stum - bling.
I will lift up the cup of full sal - va - tion.
I am your faith - ful ser - vant, freed from bon - dage.

An - guished by death and o - ver-come by sor - row,
Rest, O my soul, and trust him for sal - va - tion.
I kept my faith, though I was much af - flict - ed.
I will ful - fill my vows to God my Sa - vior.
I'll pay my vows and, with your peo - ple thank you.

I turned in my dis - tress to God in prayer.
Re - mem - ber all his good - ness shown to you.
Dis - mayed, I said, "All peo - ple are un - true."
With all his saints I'll call up - on his name.
Come to his house, O peo - ple, praise the LORD!

Words: Psalm 116; vers. Helen Otte (1980). © 1987 Faith Alive Christian Resources
Music: Genevan Psalter (1562); harm. Seymour Swets (1954), P.D.

10 11 11 10
GENEVAN 116

This psalm of personal thanksgiving and praise is part of the eight "Halleluia" psalms (111-118). Likely written after healing from a deathly illness, it is rich in Passover imagery such as the "cup of salvation." Otte prepared the strikingly unrhymed versification for the 1987 *Psalter Hymnal*, while Swets made the harmonization of this much-loved Genevan tune for the 1959 *Psalter Hymnal*.

Psalm 130: Out of the Depths I Cry to You   10

1 Out of the depths I cry to you: O Lord, now hear me call - ing.
2 All things you send are full of grace; you crown our lives with fa - vor.
3 It is in God that we shall hope, and not in our own mer - it.
4 My soul is wait-ing for the Lord as one who longs for morn - ing;

In - cline your ear to my dis - tress in spite of my re - bel - ling.
All our good works are done in vain with-out our Lord and Sav - ior.
We rest our fears in God's good Word and trust the Ho - ly Spir - it,
no watch-er waits with great - er hope than I for Christ's re - turn - ing.

Do not re - gard my sin - ful deeds. Send me the grace my
We praise the God who gives us faith and saves us from the
whose prom - ise keeps us strong and sure; we trust the ho - ly
I hope as Is - rael in the Lord, who sends re - demp-tion

spir - it needs; with - out it I am noth - ing.
grip of death; our lives are in God's keep - ing.
sig - na - ture in - scribed up - on our tem - ples.
through the Word. Praise God for end - less mer - cy.

Words: Martin Luther (1524); tr. Gracia Grindal (Ps. 130; 120:1-2) © 1978 *Lutheran Book of Worship*   87 87 887
Music: Martin Luther (1524); harm. Austin C. Lovelace (1963) © 1964 Abingdon Press   AUS TIEFER NOT

One of the famous penitential psalms, and apparently one that Luther loved, Psalm 130 was freely paraphrased and revised by him in the earliest Lutheran hymnals. He also composed the tune which, given the text, has surprisingly spritely rhythms.

11 Psalm 136: We Give Thanks unto You

Words: Psalm 136; vers. Marty Haugen
Music: Marty Haugen
Words and Music © 1987 GIA Publications

irregular
HAUGEN'S 136

5 You delivered the ones who called unto you,
for your love is never ending;
from bondage to freedom, you brought them forth,
for your love is never ending.

6 You have opened the sea and brought your people through:
for your love is never ending;
brought them into a land that flows with life,
for your love is never ending.

7 You remember your promise age to age:
for your love is never ending;
you show mercy on those of low degree,
for your love is never ending.

8 You give food and life to all living things:
for your love is never ending;
we give thanks unto you, the God of all,
for your love is never ending.

Psalm 136 is cast in litany form: each verse features the recurring refrain, "God's love endures forever." Haugen summarizes this psalm in this setting, but happily keeps the litany pattern. He is a distinguished composer of church music, and his compositions have found a home in both Roman Catholic and Protestant churches.

12 Psalm 147: Sing to God, with Joy

Sing to God, with joy and glad-ness, hymns and psalms of grat-i-tude;

with the voice of praise dis-cov-er that to wor-ship God is good.

Stanzas

1 God u-nites his scat-tered peo-ple, gath-ers those who wan-dered far,
2 Such is God's great power and wis-dom none can cal-cu-late or tell;

To Refrain

heals the hurt and bro-ken spir-its, tend-ing ev-ery wound and scar.
keen is God to ground the wick-ed and with hum-ble folk to dwell.

3 God with clouds the sky has curtained,
   thus ensuring rain shall fall;
   earth, responding, grows to order
   food for creatures great and small.

4 God's discernment never favors
   strength or speed to lift or move;
   God delights in those who fear him,
   trusting in his steadfast love.

Words and Music: John Bell, based on Psalm 147
© 1993 WGRG the Iona Community (Scotland) (admin. by GIA Publications, Inc.)

87 87 with refrain
GLENDON

This post-exilic psalm helps us sing the greatness and goodness of our God, who is not only Creator but also Redeemer. Bell's music features delightful syncopation (off-beat accents) over a steady "walking bass," similar to the polyphony of creational and human phenomena that are grounded in God's covenant faithfulness.

Song of Mary: Tell Out, My Soul   13

Unison

1 Tell out, my soul, the great-ness of the Lord!
2 Tell out, my soul, the great-ness of his name!
3 Tell out, my soul, the great-ness of his might!
4 Tell out, my soul, the glo-ries of his Word!

Un - num - bered bless - ings give my spir - it voice;
Make known his might, the deeds his arm has done;
Powers and do - min - ions lay their glo - ry by.
Firm is his prom - ise, and his mer - cy sure.

ten - der to me the prom - ise of his Word;
his mer - cy sure, from age to age the same;
Proud hearts and stub - born wills are put to flight,
Tell out, my soul, the great - ness of the Lord

in God my Sav - ior shall my heart re - joice.
his ho - ly name the Lord, the Might - y One.
the hun - gry fed, the hum - ble lift - ed high.
to chil - dren's chil - dren and for - ev - er - more!

Words: Luke 1:46-55 Timothy Dudley-Smith, © 1962, Renewed 1990 Hope Publishing Company.   10 10 10 10
Music: Walter Greatorex (1916), alt., P.D.   WOODLANDS

This free paraphrase of the Song of Mary is the best-known of all the Dudley-Smith hymn texts, and was in part inspired by the "Tell out, my soul" language for this canticle in the *New English Bible*. But it is undoubtedly the dramatic tune WOODLANDS that is equally to be credited for the popularity of this great hymn.

14 Song of Zechariah: Blessed Be the God of Israel

1 Blessed be the God of Is - ra - el, who comes to set us free
2 With prom-ised mer - cy will God still the cov - e - nant re - call,
3 My child, as proph-et of the Lord, you will pre-pare the way,

and rais - es up new hope for us: a Branch from Da-vid's tree.
the oath once sworn to A - bra-ham, from foes to save us all,
to tell God's peo - ple they are saved from sin's e - ter - nal sway.

So have the proph-ets long de-clared that with a might-y arm
that we might wor-ship with-out fear and of - fer lives of praise,
Then shall God's mer - cy from on high shine forth and nev - er cease

God would turn back our en - e - mies and all who wish us harm.
in ho - li - ness and right-eous - ness to serve God all our days.
to drive a - way the gloom of death and lead us in - to peace.

Words: Song of Zechariah, Luke 1:68-79; Carl P. Daw, Jr. (1989), © Hope Publishing Company.
Music: English folk Music; adapt. and harm. Ralph Vaughan Williams (1906)

86 86 D
FOREST GREEN

Also commonly known by the Latin title "Benedictus," this is one of the Lukan canticles that the Christian church has used for matins (morning prayers), given Zechariah's reference to "the rising sun." Vaughan Williams turned an old ballad melody into this cheerful hymn tune in the *English Hymnal* (1906).

Song of Simeon: 15
Lord, Bid Your Servant Go in Peace

1 Lord, bid your ser - vant go in peace; your
2 This is the Sav - ior of the world, the

word is now ful - filled. These eyes have seen sal -
Gen - tiles' prom - ised light, God's glo - ry dwell - ing

va - tion's dawn, this child so long fore - told.
in our midst, the joy of Is - ra - el.

Words: Song of Simeon, Luke 2:29-32; vers. James Quinn, SJ, alt. © 1969 Selah Publishing Co., Inc.   86 86
Music: Appalachain folk melody (19th C); harm. Annabel Morris Buchanen (1938), P.D.   LAND OF REST

This is one of the famous Lukan canticles, much used in evening services and at the end of the eucharist; this versification is unrhymed. LAND OF REST is one of the popular shape-note tunes from *The Sacred Harp* (1844) which Buchanan "rediscovered."

16 Father, We Give You Thanks, Who Planted

1 Fa - ther, we give you thanks, who plant - ed your ho - ly name with-
2 Watch o'er your church, O Lord, in mer - cy, save it from e - vil,

in our hearts; knowl - edge and faith and life im - mor - tal
guard it still; per - fect it in your love, u - nite it,

Je - sus, your Son, to us im - parts. Lord, you have made all
cleansed and con - formed un - to your will. As grain, once scat - tered

for your plea - sure, and given us food for all our days,
on the hill - sides, was in the bro - ken bread made one,

Words: F. Bland Tucker (1941), alt.; based on the Didache (ca. 110). © 1943, 1961, 1981 The Church
    Pension Fund. Used by permission.
Music: Genevan Psalter (1551); harm. *Pilgrim Hymnal* (1931), P.D.

98 98 D

GENEVAN 98/118

giv - ing in Christ the bread e - ter - nal.
so may your world - wide church be gath - ered

Yours is the power; be yours the praise.
in - to your king - dom by your Son.

Tucker's text is a translation of several prayers from the *Didache,* which is a Greek-language manual of Christian teaching and practices from Antioch, Syria. This vibrantly rhythmic tune was used for both Psalm 98 and Psalm 118 in the Genevan Psalter (1562).

17 O Gladsome Light, O Grace

1 O glad-some Light, O grace of God the Fa-ther's face,
2 As day fades in - to night, we see the eve-ning light,
3 To you of right be - longs all praise of ho - ly songs,

the e - ter - nal splen-dor wear-ing: ce - les - tial, ho - ly, blest,
our hymn of praise out - pour-ing, Fa - ther of might un - known,
O Son of God, life - giv - er; you, there-fore, O Most High,

our Sav - ior Je - sus Christ, joy - ful in your ap - pear - ing!
Christ, his in - car - nate Son, and Ho - ly Spirit a - dor - ing.
the world will glo - ri - fy and shall ex - alt for - ev - er.

Words: Greek (3rd c.); tr. Robert S. Bridges (1899) alt., P.D.
Music: Louis Bourgeois (1547); harm. Claude Goudimel (1565), P.D.

667 667
NUNC DIMITTIS

This is an example of the "lamp-lighting" hymns sung by the early Christians, who inherited this practice from the lighting of lamps in Jewish homes at the beginning of each Sabbath. It is an evening hymn, filled with imagery of light and the Trinity, suitably supported by a tune that early Calvinists used to sing to the Song of Simeon.

Shepherd of Tender Youth 18

1 Shep-herd of ten - der youth, guid-ing in love and truth
2 You are the ho - ly Lord, O all - sub - du - ing Word,
3 You are the great High Priest; you have pre - pared the feast
4 O ev - er be our Guide, our Shep-herd at our side,

through de - vious ways. Christ, our tri - um-phant king, we come your
heal - er of strife. Your-self you did a - base, that from sin's
of ho - ly love, for in our mor - tal pain none calls on
our staff and song. Je - sus, O Christ of God, by your en -

name to sing and here our chil - dren bring to join your praise.
deep dis - grace you so might save our race and give us life.
you in vain. Our plea do not dis - dain: help from a - bove!
dur - ing Word lead us where you have trod; make our faith strong.

5 So now, and till we die,
   sound we your praises high and joyful sing:
   infants and all the throng,
   who to the Church belong,
   unite to swell the song to Christ, our king!

Words: attr. Clement of Alexandria (ca. 170-220); tr. Henry M. Dexter (1853) alt., P.D.
Music: Felice de Giardini (1769), P.D.

664 6664
ITALIAN HYMN

Clement's hymn was appended to his early second century manual called *The Tutor*, in which he taught the new Christian lifestyle to the converts in the wild city of Alexandria. Dexter's translation smooths out Clement's bold language in this earliest of all post-New Testament hymns. For notes on the tune, see "Come, Thou Almighty King" (102).

19 All Glory Be to God on High

1 All glo - ry be to God on high, and peace on earth from
2 O Lamb of God, Lord Je - sus Christ, whom God the Fa - ther
3 You on - ly are the Ho - ly One who came for our sal-

heav - en, and God's good-will un - fail - ing - ly be to his
gave us, who for the world was sac - ri - ficed up - on the
va - tion, and on - ly you are God's true Son who was be -

peo - ple giv - en. Al - might - y God, you are our King: we
cross to save us, at God's right hand you in - ter - cede for
fore cre - a - tion. You on - ly, Christ, as Lord we own, and

wor - ship you, our thanks we bring, we praise you for your glo - ry.
those who for your mer - cy plead; re - ceive the prayer we of - fer.
with the Spir - it you a - lone share in the Fa - ther's glo - ry.

Words: Latin: Gloria in excelsis Deo (4th c.); vers. Nikolaus Decius (1525);
tr. F. Bland Tucker (1977), alt. © 1985 The Church Pension Fund.
Music: attr. Nikolaus Decius (1539), P.D.

87 87 887

ALLEIN GOTT IN DER HOH' SEI EHR

The Latin hymn "Gloria in excelsis Deo" became part of the fixed texts of the medieval Roman Catholic mass, which Luther wanted translated into German. A student of Luther, Decius made such a translation and fashioned it with a tune adapted from a tenth-century Easter chant for the "Gloria."

Holy God, We Praise Your Name 20

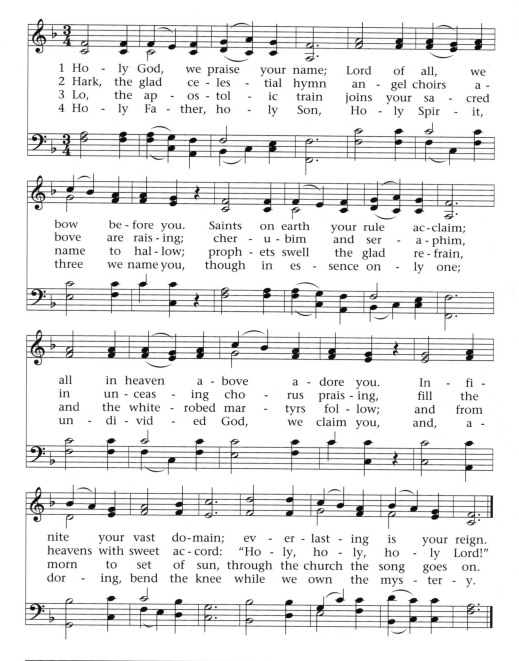

1 Ho - ly God, we praise your name; Lord of all, we
2 Hark, the glad ce - les - tial hymn an - gel choirs a -
3 Lo, the ap - os - tol - ic train joins your sa - cred
4 Ho - ly Fa - ther, ho - ly Son, Ho - ly Spir - it,

bow be - fore you. Saints on earth your rule ac - claim;
bove are rais - ing; cher - u - bim and ser - a - phim,
name to hal - low; proph - ets swell the glad re - frain,
three we name you, though in es - sence on - ly one;

all in heaven a - bove a - dore you. In - fi -
in un - ceas - ing cho - rus prais - ing, fill the
and the white - robed mar - tyrs fol - low; and from
un - di - vid - ed God, we claim you, and, a -

nite your vast do - main; ev - er - last - ing is your reign.
heavens with sweet ac - cord: "Ho - ly, ho - ly, ho - ly Lord!"
morn to set of sun, through the church the song goes on.
dor - ing, bend the knee while we own the mys - ter - y.

Words: Te Deum (4th c.); vers. Ignaz Franz (1774); tr. Clarence A. Walworth (1853), alt. P.D. 78 78 77
Music: *Katholisches Gesangbuch*, Vienna (1774), P.D. GROSSER GOTT

Franz, a Roman Catholic priest, translated the Latin original into German (beginning "Grosser Gott, wir loben dich") for a Viennese hymnal that is also the source of the tune. Eventually Walworth translated the text somewhat loosely into English for a U.S. Roman Catholic hymnal. Rooted in ancient Christianity, this classic text of faith is used in the worship of God by all traditions of Christianity: Orthodox, Roman Catholic, and Protestant.

21 O Splendor of God's Glory Bright

1 O splen - dor of God's glo - ry bright, from light e -
2 Come, ver - y Sun of heav - en's love, in last - ing
3 Con - firm our will to do the right, and keep our
4 All praise to God the Fa - ther be, all praise, e -

ter - nal bring - ing light; O Light of light, the
ra - diance from a - bove, and pour the Ho - ly
hearts from en - vy's blight; let faith her ea - ger
ter - nal Son, to thee, whom with the Spir - it

foun - tain spring, O Day, all days il - lu - min - ing.
Spir - it's ray on all we think or do to - day.
fires re - new, and hate the false, and love the true.
we a - dore for - ev - er and for - ev - er - more.

Words: Ambrose of Milan (4th c.); tr. composite, P.D.
Music: Trier manuscript (15th c.); adapt. Michael Praetorius (1609), P.D.

88 88
PUER NOBIS

Wrapped in imagery of light and the Trinity, this is a famous morning hymn, penned in Latin by Ambrose, the bishop of Milan, who was a strong proponent of congregational song. The German melody was used by Praetorius in his *Musae Sioniae* (1609) for a Christmas carol that in English became "Unto Us a Boy Is Born;" a slightly different harmonization is used for "That Easter Day with Joy Was Bright" (25).

Savior of the Nations, Come 22

1 Sav - ior of the na - tions, come, show your -
2 Not by hu - man power or seed did the
3 Mar - y then was found with child, still a
4 Christ laid down his maj - es - ty, passed through

self, the vir - gin's son. Fill with won - der,
wom - an's womb con - ceive; on - ly by the
vir - gin, chaste and mild. God had fa - vored
dark Geth - sem - a - ne. Though he left his

all the earth, that our God chose such a birth.
Spir - it's breath was the Word of God made flesh.
her with grace to re - ceive the Prince of Peace.
Fa - ther's home, Christ now sits on God's own throne.

5 Since the star at Bethlehem
  brought new light to earth again,
  may our faith shine bright each day;
  faithful God, keep sin away.

6 Christ in glory, intercede
  for your creatures' suffering need.
  Let your resurrecting power
  soon complete the victory hour.

7 Praise to you, O Lord, we sing.
  Praise to Christ, our newborn King!
  With the Father, Spirit, one,
  let your lasting kingdom come.

Words: Ambrose (4th c.), and Martin Luther (1523); tr. Calvin Seerveld (1984) © Calvin Seerveld   77 77
Music: *Enchiridia*, Erfurt (1524); harm. Seth Calvisius (1594), P.D.   NUN KOMM DER HEIDEN HEILAND

As attested by Augustine, Ambrose, the bishop of Milan, wrote this famous Advent hymn, "Veni, Redemptor Gentium." Luther translated the Latin text into German and set it to a tune derived from chant. There are numerous English translations; the one featured here was prepared by Seerveld for the *Psalter Hymnal* (1987).

23   Of the Father's Love Begotten

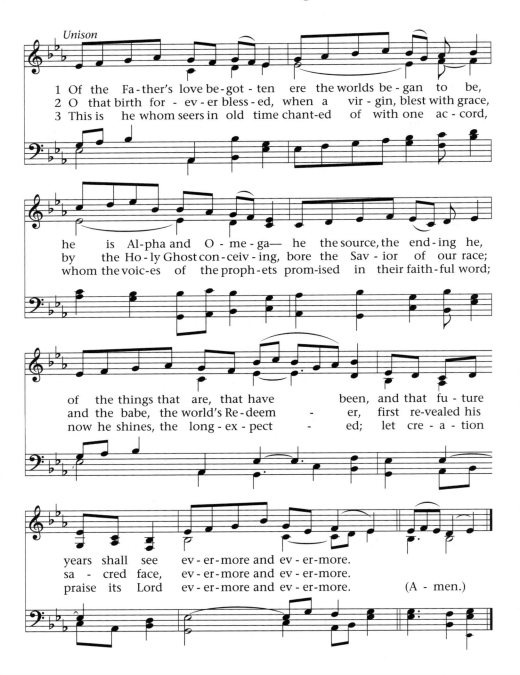

Unison

1 Of the Fa-ther's love be-got-ten   ere the worlds be-gan to be,
2 O that birth for - ev - er bless-ed, when a   vir - gin, blest with grace,
3 This is   he whom seers in old time chant-ed   of with one ac - cord,

he   is Al-pha and O - me-ga— he   the source, the end-ing he,
by   the Ho - ly Ghost con-ceiv-ing, bore the Sav - ior of our race;
whom the voic-es of the proph-ets prom-ised in their faith-ful word;

of   the things that are, that have   been, and that fu - ture
and the babe, the world's Re-deem   -   er, first re-vealed his
now he shines, the long - ex - pect   -   ed; let cre - a - tion

years shall see   ev-er-more and ev-er-more.
sa - cred face,   ev-er-more and ev-er-more.
praise its Lord   ev-er-more and ev-er-more.   (A - men.)

Words: Marcus Aurelius C. Prudentius (4th c.); tr. John M. Neale (1854),
   and Henry W. Baker (1859), alt., P.D.
Music: 12th c. Plainsong; arr. C. Winfred Douglas (1916) © 1943, 1961, 1981
   The Church Pension Fund

87 87 877

DIVINUM MYSTERIUM

4 Let the heights of heaven adore him;
  angel hosts, his praises sing:
  powers, dominions, bow before him
  and extol our God and King;
  let no tongue on earth be silent,
  every voice in concert ring
  evermore and evermore.

5 Christ, to you, with God the Father
  and the Spirit, there shall be
  hymn and chant and high thanksgiving
  and the shout of jubilee;
  honor, glory, and dominion
  and eternal victory
  evermore and evermore! Amen.

A famous example of his many poetic writings, Prudentius' text is a confession of faith about Christ, whose birth and saving ministry were the fulfillment of ancient prophecies. Two doxological stanzas complete this great Christmas hymn, commonly sung to a chant melody that appears in modern hymnals in either a dance-like triple meter or, as here, in unmeasured form that should follow speech rhythms.

24 Let All Mortal Flesh Keep Silence

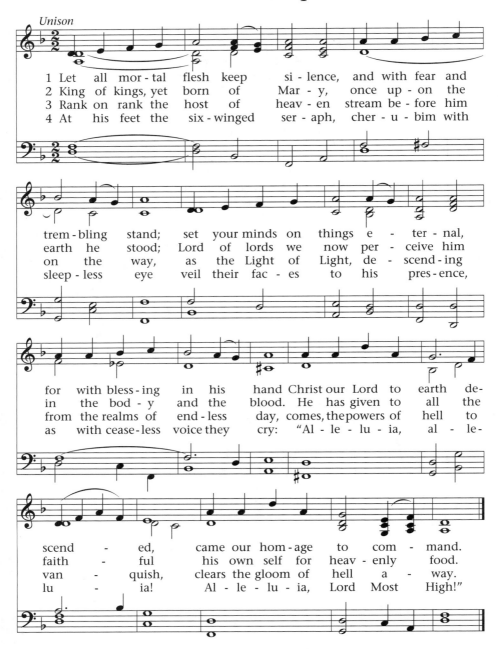

Unison

1 Let all mor-tal flesh keep si-lence, and with fear and
2 King of kings, yet born of Mar-y, once up-on the
3 Rank on rank the host of heav-en stream be-fore him
4 At his feet the six-winged ser-aph, cher-u-bim with

trem-bling stand; set your minds on things e-ter-nal,
earth he stood; Lord of lords we now per-ceive him
on the way, as the Light of Light, de-scend-ing
sleep-less eye veil their fac-es to his pres-ence,

for with bless-ing in his hand Christ our Lord to earth de-
in the bod-y and the blood. He has given to all the
from the realms of end-less day, comes, the powers of hell to
as with cease-less voice they cry: "Al-le-lu-ia, al-le-

scend - ed, came our hom-age to com - mand.
faith - ful his own self for heav-enly food.
van - quish, clears the gloom of hell a - way.
lu - ia! Al-le-lu-ia, Lord Most High!"

Words: Liturgy of St. James; tr. Gerard Moultrie (1864), P.D.
Music: French (17th c.), *Chansons Populaires des Provinces de France* (1860), P.D.

87 87 87
PICARDY

Originally Greek, this text is derived from the "Cherubic Hymn" used in the Eastern Orthodox rite of St. James when the communion elements are brought into the sanctuary. In singing this hymn we are drawn into the mystery of Christ's coming. The marriage of this ancient text with this French noël melody was consecrated by Ralph Vaughan Williams in the *English Hymnal* (1906), from which the harmonization was adapted. The same tune is used for "You, Lord, Are Both Lamb and Shepherd" (248).

That Easter Day with Joy Was Bright 25

1 That Eas - ter day with joy was bright,
2 His ris - en flesh with ra - diance glowed,
3 O Je - sus, strong in gen - tle - ness,
4 Come, ris - en Christ, with us a - bide

the sun shone out with fair - er light,
his wound - ed hands and feet he showed,
come now your - self our hearts pos - sess,
in this our joy - ful Eas - ter - tide;

when, to their long - ing eyes re - stored,
those scars their sol - emn wit - ness gave
that we will give you all our days
your own re - deemed for - ev - er shield

the glad a - pos - tles saw their Lord.
that Christ was ris - en from the grave.
the trib - ute of our grate - ful praise.
from ev - ery weap - on death can wield.

Words: Latin hymn (5th c.); tr. John M. Neale (1852), alt. P.D.
Music: Trier manuscript (15th c.); adapt. Michael Praetorius (1609); harm. George R.
    Woodward (1910), P.D.

88 88
PUER NOBIS

This ancient Easter hymn focuses on Jesus' post-resurrection appearances to his disciples and concludes with a prayer for Christ to abide with us. It comes from a long Latin poem that meditates on various aspects of the Easter gospel. For the music with a slightly different harmonization, see "O Splendor of God's Glory Bright" (21).

26   I Bind unto Myself Today

1 I bind un-to my-self to-day the strong name of the Trin-i-ty by in-vo-ca-tion of the same, the Three in One and One in Three.

2 I bind this day to me for-ev-er, by power of faith, Christ's in-car-na-tion, his bap-tism in the Jor-dan Riv-er, his cross of death for my sal-va-tion, his burst-ing from the spic-ed tomb, his rid-ing up the heaven-ly way, his com-ing at the day of doom, I bind un-to my-self to-day.

3 I bind un-to my-self to-day the vir-tues of the star-lit heav-en, the glo-rious sun's life-giv-ing ray, the white-ness of the moon at e-ven, the flash-ing of the light-ning free, the whirl-ing wind's tem-pes-tuous shocks, the sta-ble earth, the deep salt sea, a-round the old e-ter-nal rocks.

4 Christ be with me, Christ with-in me, Christ be-neath me, Christ a-bove me, Christ be-Christ in

Words: attr. Patrick of Ireland (432); tr. and para. Cecil F. Alexander (1889), P.D.
Music: sts. 1-3, 5: trad. Irish, *The Complete Petrie Collection of Ancient Irish Music* (1902), P.D.
st. 4: trad. Irish, *Ancient Music of Ireland* (1848), P.D.

sts. 1-3, 5 irregular
ST. PATRICK'S BREASTPLATE

st. 4 88 88
DEIRDRE

hind me, Christ be-fore me, Christ be-side me, Christ to
qui - et, Christ in dan - ger, Christ in hearts of all that

win me, Christ to com - fort and re - store me,
love me, Christ in mouth of friend and stran - ger.

5 I bind un-to my-self the name, the strong name of the Trin-i-

ty, by in - vo - ca - tion of the same, the Three in

One and One in Three, of whom all na - ture has cre -

a - tion, e - ter - nal Fa - ther, Spir - it, Word. Praise to the

Lord of my sal - va-tion; sal - va - tion is of Christ the Lord!

Apocryphally attributed to the legendary Patrick, this text from the eleventh century is a rich mixture of Trinitarian appropriation, narrative Christology, and remnants of Celtic creational spirituality. This setting provides two traditional Irish melodies, one for unison singing (harmony available in various other hymnals) and the other in harmony. The "Christ be with me" segment could also be used as an antiphon at the beginning and the end of the hymn, or alternatively, by itself alone as a prayer and affirmation of the presence of Christ in our lives.

27 Creator of the Stars of Night

5 To God the Father, God the Son,
and God the Spirit, Three-in-One,
praise, honor, might, and glory be
from age to age eternally.

Words: Latin "Conditor Alme Siderum" (6th c.); tr. John M. Neale (1852), alt., P.D.   88 88
Music: Sarum plainsong, Mode 4 (9th c.); harm. John Henry Arnold (1927), P.D.   CONDITOR ALME SIDERUM

This hymn comes from the tradition of singing during the Daily Office, in this case for Vespers during Advent.
Sing this chant tune dynamically in four phrases, observing speech rhythms—not in the strict eighth-note rhythms
that the notation might suggest.

Hark! A Thrilling Voice Is Sounding 28

1 Hark! A thrill-ing voice is sound-ing! "Christ is
near," we hear it say. "Cast a - way the
works of dark - ness, all you chil-dren of the day!"

2 Star - tled at the sol - emn warn - ing, from the
dark - ness we a - rise; Christ, our sun, all
ill dis - pel - ling, shines up - on the morn-ing skies.

3 See, the Lamb so long ex - pect - ed comes with
par - don down from heaven. Let us haste, with
tears of sor - row, one and all, to be for - given;

4 so when next he comes in glo - ry and the
world is wrapped in fear, he will shield us
with his mer - cy and with words of love draw near.

5 Honor, glory, might, dominion
to the Father and the Son,
with the everliving Spirit
while eternal ages run.

Words: Latin, "Vox Clara Eece Intonat" (6th c.); tr. *Hymns Ancient and Modern* (1861), alt., P.D. 87 87
Music: William H. Monk (1850), P.D. MERTON

As does the Bible in its foretelling of the coming of Christ, this Advent hymn includes references to Christ's first coming and his coming again. Though composed earlier, the tune was united to this text by Monk for *Hymns Ancient and Modern* (1861); that union has remained in all modern hymnals.

29 Praise the Savior Now and Ever

1 Praise the Sav - ior now and ev - er; praise him, all be -
2 Our work fail - eth, Christ's a - vail - eth; he is all our
3 Sin's bonds sev - ered, we're de - liv - ered; Christ has crushed the
4 For his fa - vor, praise for - ev - er un - to God the

neath the skies; self de - ny - ing, suf - fering, dy - ing,
right - eous - ness. He, our Sav - ior, has for - ev - er
ser - pent's head. Death no lon - ger is the stron - ger;
Fa - ther sing. Praise the Sav - ior, praise him ev - er,

on the cross a sac - ri - fice. Vic - tory gain - ing,
set us free from dire dis - tress. Through his mer - it
hell it - self is cap - tive led. Christ has ris - en
Son of God, our Lord and King. Praise the Spir - it;

life ob - tain - ing, now in glo - ry he doth rise!
we in - her - it light and peace and hap - pi - ness.
from death's pris - on; o'er the tomb he light has shed.
through Christ's mer - it he doth us sal - va - tion bring.

Words: Venantius Honorius Fortunatus (569); tr. Augustus Nelson (1925), alt., P.D.
Music: *Then Swenska Psalm-Boken*, Stockholm (1697), P.D.

87 87 87
UPP, MIN TUNGA

Fortunatus' "Pange, Lingua, Glorioso Proelium" was written in Latin, transformed in Swedish from a focus on Christ's passion to his resurrection, and ultimately translated into English for the *Hymnal* of the Augustana Luther-an Synod (1925). The Swedish tune originally had dotted rhythms that are, unfortunately, lost in the isorhythmic (equal quarter notes) setting given here.

A Great and Mighty Wonder 30

1 A great and might-y won-der, a full and ho-ly cure:
2 The Word be-comes in-car-nate and yet re-mains on high,
3 While thus they sing your mon-arch, those bright an-gel-ic bands,

the vir-gin bears the in-fant with vir-gin hon-or pure!
and cher-u-bim sing an-thems to shep-herds from the sky.
re-joice, O vales and moun-tains, and o-ceans, clap your hands.

Refrain

Re-peat the hymn a-gain: "To God on

high be glo-ry and peace on earth to men!"

4 Since all he comes to ransom,
by all be he adored,
the infant born in Bethlehem,
the Savior and the Lord. *Refrain*

5 All idol forms shall perish
and error's arguing,
and Christ shall wield his scepter,
our Lord, our God, our King! *Refrain*

Words: Germanus (ca. 634-734); tr. John M. Neale (1862), alt., P.D.
Music: *Alte Catholische Geistliche Kirchengesäng*, Köln (1599), P.D.

76 76 6 76
ES IST EIN ROS ENTSPRUNGEN

Germanus' Greek text "The Divine Paradox" was translated by Neale into six stanzas in his *Hymns from the Eastern Church*. Stanza 3 became the refrain when this text was united to ES IST EIN' ROS' ENTSPRUNGEN in the *English Hymnal* (1906). That folk tune from a Roman Catholic songbook is commonly associated with "Lo, How a Rose E'er Blooming" (53).

31 A Hymn of Glory Let Us Sing!

1 A hymn of glo-ry let us sing!
2 The ho-ly ap-os-to-lic band
3 O Lord, our home-ward path-way bend
4 O ris-en Christ, as-cend-ed Lord,

New hymns through-out the world shall ring:
up-on the Mount of Ol-ives stand,
that our un-wear-ied hearts as-cend,
all praise to you let earth ac-cord:

Al-le-lu-ia! Al-le-lu-ia!

Christ, by a road be-fore un-trod,
and with his faith-ful fol-lowers see
where, seat-ed on your Fa-ther's throne,
You are, while end-less a-ges run,

Words: *Bede of Jarrow* (673-735); tr. *Lutheran Book of Worship* (1978) © 1978 *Lutheran Book of Worship* (admin. by Augsburg Fortress)
Music: *Auserlesen Geistliche Kirchengesäng*, Cologne (1623); harm. Ralph Vaughan Williams (1906), P.D.

88 88 with alleluias

LASST UNS ERFREUEN

as - cends un - to the throne of God.
their Lord as - cend in maj - es - ty.
you reign as King of kings a - lone.
with Fa - ther and with Spir - it one.

Refrain
Harmony

Al - le - lu - ia! Al - le - lu - ia! Al - le - lu - ia,

Unison

al - le - lu - ia, al - le - lu - ia!

Originally in Latin ("Hymnum canamus gloriae"), this Ascension hymn was written by the "venerable" Bede, a harp-playing monk from Jarrow, England, who is best known as a historian of early British Christianity. For information on the tune, see "All Creatures of Our God and King" (41), in E♭ major.

32 Be Thou My Vision

1 Be thou my vi - sion, O Lord of my heart;
2 Be thou my wis - dom, and thou my true word;
3 Rich - es I heed not, nor vain, emp - ty praise;
4 High King of heav - en, my vic - to - ry won,

naught be all else to me, save that thou art—
I ev - er with thee and thou with me, Lord.
thou mine in - her - i - tance, now and al - ways:
may I reach heav - en's joys, O bright heaven's sun!

thou my best thought, by day or by night;
Thou my great Fa - ther; thine own may I be,
thou and thou on - ly, first in my heart,
Heart of my own heart, what - ev - er be - fall,

wak - ing or sleep - ing, thy pres - ence my light.
thou in me dwell - ing, and I one with thee.
high King of heav - en, my treas - ure thou art.
still be my vi - sion, O Rul - er of all.

Words: Irish (8th c.); tr. Mary E. Byrne (1905); vers. Eleanor H. Hull (1912), alt. P.D.
Music: trad. Irish folk melody; harm. Jack Schrader (1989) © 1989 Hope Publishing Company.

10 10 10 10
SLANE

Through both direct names and metaphors for Christ, this hymn helps us pray that in all of our life we may focus on Jesus. This text was first wed to the fine Irish tune SLANE in the *Church Hymnary* (1927) and has become a very popular Christian hymn.

Christ Is Made the Sure Foundation 33

1 Christ is made the sure foun-da - tion, Christ, our head and
2 To this tem - ple, where we call you, come, O Lord of
3 Here be-stow on all your ser - vants what they seek from
4 Praise and hon - or to the Fa - ther, praise and hon - or

cor - ner - stone, cho - sen of the Lord and pre - cious,
hosts, and stay; come with all your lov - ing-kind-ness,
you to gain. What they gain from you, for - ev - er
to the Son, praise and hon - or to the Spir - it,

bind - ing all the Church in one; ho - ly Zi - on's
hear your peo - ple as they pray, and your full - est
with the bless - ed to re - tain; and here - af - ter
ev - er three and ev - er one: one in might and

help for - ev - er and our con - fi - dence a - lone.
ben - e - dic - tion shed with-in these walls to - day.
in your glo - ry ev - er-more with you to reign.
one in glo - ry while un-end - ing a - ges run!

Words: Latin, "Angularis Fundamentum", (8th c.); tr. John M. Neale (1851), alt., P.D.   87 87 87
Music: Henry Purcell (ca. 1692), P.D.   WESTMINSTER ABBEY

This text comes from a Latin hymn originally used for the dedication of church buildings, but the New Testament imagery of Christ as the cornerstone of his church, i.e., his body or people, is most convincing. Purcell's fine tune is an extract of one of his anthems made by Vincent Novello (1843); the union of this text and tune has gained much popularity in twentieth-century hymnals.

34 Come, Ye Faithful, Raise the Strain

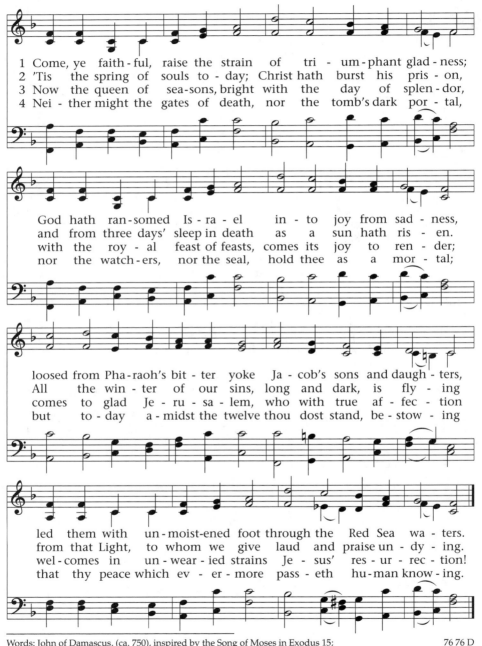

Words: John of Damascus, (ca. 750), inspired by the Song of Moses in Exodus 15;
 tr. John M. Neale (1859), alt., P.D.
Music: German, Joham Horn's *Gesanglouch* (1955), P.D.

76 76 D

GAUDEAMUS PARITER

This text, intended for the Sunday after Easter ("doubting" Thomas), is from John's Greek canon (an extended hymn based on biblical canticles) in which he explains how Old Testament prophecies were fulfilled in Christ's resurrection. The lively tune comes from an early Moravian hymnal.

All Glory, Laud, and Honor 35

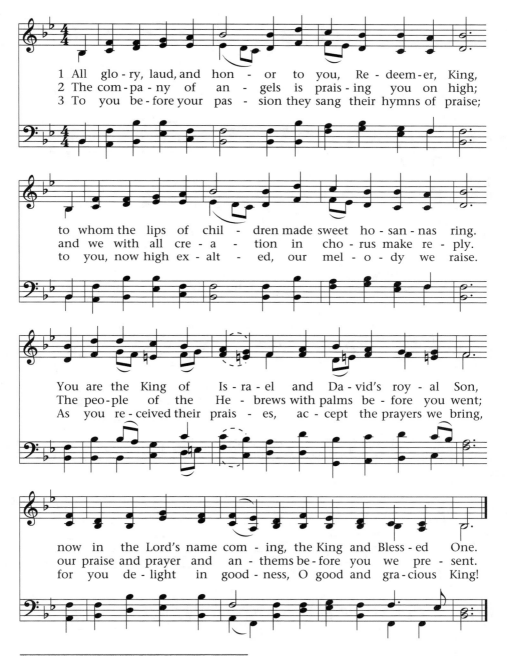

1 All glo-ry, laud, and hon - or to you, Re - deem-er, King,
2 The com-pa-ny of an - gels is prais-ing you on high;
3 To you be-fore your pas - sion they sang their hymns of praise;

to whom the lips of chil - dren made sweet ho-san-nas ring.
and we with all cre-a - tion in cho-rus make re - ply.
to you, now high ex-alt - ed, our mel - o - dy we raise.

You are the King of Is - ra - el and Da - vid's roy - al Son,
The peo-ple of the He - brews with palms be - fore you went;
As you re-ceived their prais - es, ac - cept the prayers we bring,

now in the Lord's name com - ing, the King and Bless - ed One.
our praise and prayer and an - thems be-fore you we pre - sent.
for you de-light in good - ness, O good and gra-cious King!

Words: Theodulph of Orleans, (ca. 820); tr. John M. Neale (1851), alt., P.D.   76 76 D
Music: Melchior Teschner (1615); harm. William H. Monk (1861), P.D.   ST. THEODULPH

A bishop of Orleans, Theodulph wrote this text for Palm Sunday while imprisoned in Angers, France. Legend has
it that King Louis the Pious heard Theodulph sing this text and set him free. Teschner's melody is a vigorous tune
that Monk harmonized for the union of this text and tune in *Hymns Ancient and Modern*.

36 O Holy Spirit, By Whose Breath

1 O Holy Spirit, by whose breath
2 You are the seeker's only course,
3 In you God's energy is shown,
4 Flood our dull senses with your light;

life rises vibrant out of death,
of burning love the living source,
to us your varied gifts made known.
in mutual love our hearts unite.

come to create, renew, inspire;
protector in the midst of strife,
Teach us to speak, teach us to hear;
Your power the whole creation fills;

Words: Latin hymn, "Veni Creator Spiritus," (9th c.); tr. John W. Grant (1968), alt., © John W. Grant   88 88
Music: Mechlin plainsong, Mode 8; harm. Healey Willian © 1995   VENI CREATOR SPIRITUS

come, kin - dle in   our hearts   your fire.
the   giv - er and   the   Lord   of   life.
yours be the tongue   and yours   the   ear.
make strong our weak,   un - cer - tain wills.

5 From inner strife grant us release;
   turn nations to the ways of peace.
   To fuller life your people bring
   that as one body we may sing:

6 Praise to the Father, Christ, his Word,
   and to the Spirit: God the Lord,
   to whom all honor, glory be
   both now and for eternity.

Grant wrote his translation of this famous Latin invocation of the Holy Spirit for *The Hymn Book* of the Canadian
Anglican and United Churches (1971). The chant melody used here is from *Vesperale Romanum* (1848), a collection
of plainsong melodies modified for use by French Roman Catholics who were unfamiliar with the chant idiom.

37 O Come, O Come, Immanuel

1 O come, O come, Im-man - u - el, and ran-som cap - tive
2 O come, O Wis-dom from on high, who or-dered all things
3 O come, O come, great Lord of might, who to your tribes on

Is - ra - el that mourns in lone - ly ex - ile here
might - i - ly; to us the path of knowl - edge show
Si - nai's height in an - cient times did give the law

Refrain

un - til the Son of God ap - pear.
and teach us in its ways to go. Re - joice! Re - joice! Im-
in cloud and maj - es - ty and awe.

man - u - el shall come to you, O Is - ra - el.

Words: Latin, "Veni, Veni Immanuel" (12th c.); tr. composite, P.D.
Music: *Processionale* (15th); adapt. Thomas Helmore (1854), P.D.

88 88 with refrain
VENI IMMANUEL

4 O come, O Branch of Jesse's stem,
 unto your own and rescue them!
 From depths of hell your people save,
 and give them victory o'er the grave.
 Refrain

5 O come, O Key of David, come
 and open wide our heavenly home.
 Make safe for us the heavenward road
 and bar the way to death's abode.
 Refrain

6 O come, O Bright and Morning Star,
 and bring us comfort from afar!
 Dispel the shadows of the night
 and turn our darkness into light.
 Refrain

7 O come, O King of nations, bind
 in one the hearts of all mankind.
 Bid all our sad divisions cease
 and be yourself our King of Peace.
 Refrain

Possibly dating back to a Jewish-Christian celebration of Hanukkah in the fifth century, this great Advent text sets out Old Testament names for the coming Messiah, with each stanza originally tied to one of the seven "Great 'O' Antiphons," which were sung with the Song of Mary during Vespers. The melody comes from a requiem mass in a French Franciscan collection of chants.

38 The God of Abraham Praise

1 The God of A-braham praise, who reigns en-throned a-bove,
2 He by his name has sworn, on this we shall de-pend,
3 The good-ly land I see, with peace and plen-ty blest,

the An-cient of e-ter-nal days, the God of love!
and as on ea-gles' wings up-borne to heaven as-cend.
a land of sa-cred lib-er-ty and end-less rest.

The Lord, the great I AM, by earth and heaven con-fessed—
There we shall see his face, his power we shall a-dore
There milk and hon-ey flow, and oil and wine a-bound;

we bow be-fore his ho-ly name for-ev-er blest.
and sing the won-ders of his grace for-ev-er-more.
the tree of life for-ev-er grows with mer-cy crowned.

Words: Jewish doxology (12th c.); tr. Thomas Olivers (ca. 1770), alt., P.D.
Music: Hebrew; adapt. Meyer Lyon (ca. 1770), P.D.

66 84 D
LEONI

4 There rules the Lord our King, the Lord our Righteousness,
   victorious over death and sin, the Prince of Peace.
   On Zion's sacred height his kingdom he maintains,
   and glorious with his saints in light forever reigns.

5 Triumphant hosts on high give thanks to God and sing,
   and "Holy, holy, holy" cry, "Almighty King!"
   Hail, Abraham's God and ours! One mighty hymn we raise.
   All power and majesty be yours and endless praise!

Moses ben Maimon formulated this doxology; it then became the twelve-stanza "Yigdal Elohim" still used in
Jewish worship. Olivers freely translated the text with a Christian viewpoint and asked a synagogue cantor, Meyer
Lyon [Leoni] to provide a suitable melody; it is a magnificent tune with lots of life and vibrant rhythms.

39 O Sacred Head, Now Wounded

1 O sa - cred head, now wound - ed, with grief and shame weighed down,
2 My Lord, what you did suf - fer was all for sin - ners' gain;
3 What lan - guage shall I bor - row to thank you, dear - est Friend,

now scorn - ful - ly sur - round - ed with thorns, your on - ly crown.
mine, mine was the trans - gres - sion, but yours the dead - ly pain.
for this, your dy - ing sor - row, your mer - cy with - out end?

O sa - cred head, what glo - ry and bless - ing you have known!
So here I kneel, my Sav - ior, for I de - serve your place;
Lord, make me yours for - ev - er, a loy - al ser - vant true,

Yet, though de - spised and gor - y, I claim you as my own.
look on me with your fa - vor and save me by your grace.
and let me nev - er, nev - er out - live my love for you.

Words: Latin "Salve Caput Cruentatum" (medieval); German tr. Paul Gerhardt (1656);
  tr. James W. Alexander (1830), alt., P.D.
Music: Hans L. Hassler (1601); adapt. and harm. Johann S. Bach (1729), P.D.

76 76 D
HERZLICH TUT MICH

The Latin poem has been attributed to Bernard of Clairvaux (c. 1091-1153) as well as to Arnulf von Loewen (1200-1251). It consists of a series of devotions on parts of Jesus' crucified body—a literary crucifix—which, in this case, focuses on Jesus' head. It is one of the great texts about Christ's passion, united to the melody of a love song transformed into a Lutheran hymn-tune, which Bach used extensively in his Passion music with various harmonizations.

Jerusalem the Golden 40

1 Je - ru - sa - lem the gold - en, de - scend - ing from a - bove,
2 They stand, those halls of Zi - on, all ju - bi - lant with song,
3 There is the throne of Da - vid, and there, from pain re - leased,
4 How love - ly is that cit - y, the home of God's e - lect!

the cit - y of God's pres - ence, the vi - sion of God's love—
so bright with man - y an an - gel and all the mar - tyr throng.
the shout of those who tri - umph, the song of those who feast.
How beau - ti - ful the coun - try that ea - ger hearts ex - pect!

I know not, oh, I know not what joys a - wait us there,
The Prince is ev - er in them, the day - light is se - rene;
And all who with their lead - er have con - quered in the fight,
O Christ, in mer - cy bring us to that e - ter - nal shore

what ra - dian - cy of glo - ry, what bliss be - yond com - pare!
the tree of life and heal - ing has leaves of rich - est green.
for - ev - er and for - ev - er are robed in pur - est white.
where Fa - ther, Son, and Spir - it are wor - shiped ev - er - more.

Words: Bernard of Cluny, (ca. 1145); tr. John M. Neale (1858), alt., P.D.
Music: Alexander Ewing (1853), P.D.

76 76 D
EWING

Bernard's text is derived from the initial stanzas of his long satiric poem, "De Contemptu Mundi," in which he contrasts the glory of heaven with the evils of his culture. The lasting union of Neale's translation with Ewing's tune was forged in *Hymns Ancient and Modern* (1861).

41 All Creatures of Our God and King

1 All crea-tures of our God and King, lift up your voice
2 O rush-ing wind so wild and strong, white clouds that sail
3 Cool flow-ing wa-ter, pure and clear, make mu-sic for

with us and sing: al-le-lu – ia, al-le-lu – ia!
in heaven a – long, al-le-lu – ia, al-le-lu – ia!
your Lord to hear; al-le-lu – ia, al-le-lu – ia!

O burn-ing sun with gold-en beam, and shin-ing moon
New ris-ing dawn, in praise re-joice; you lights of eve-
Fierce fire, so mas-ter-ful and bright, pro-vid-ing us

with sil – ver gleam, O praise him, O praise him,
ning, find a voice: O praise him, O praise him,
with warmth and light, O praise him, O praise him,

Words: Francis of Assisi (1225); tr. William H. Draper (c. 1910), alt., P.D.
Music: *Auserlesen Catholische Geistliche Kirchengesäng,* Cologne (1623);
  adapt. and harm. Ralph Vaughan Williams (1906), P.D.

88 88 with alleluias
LASST UNS ERFREUEN

Unison

al - le - lu - ia,   al - le - lu - ia,   al - le - lu - ia!

4 Earth ever fertile, day by day
  bring forth your blessings on our way;
  alleluia, alleluia!
  All flowers and fruits that in you grow,
  let them his glory also show;
  O praise him, O praise him,
  alleluia, *(3x)*

5 People and nations take your part;
  sing praise to God with all your heart:
  alleluia, alleluia!
  Let all things their Creator bless
  and worship him in lowliness;
  O praise him, O praise him,
  alleluia, *(3x)*

Inspired by Psalms 145 and 148, as well as by the "Canticle of the Three Young Men" (apocryphal addition to
Daniel 3), Francis' "Canticle of the Sun" is a catalogue hymn in which various facets of creation are urged to praise
the Lord with their "alleluias." The powerful tune (which shows similarity to the Genevan tune for Psalm 68)
comes from an early Jesuit hymnal. For this tune in D major, see "A Hymn of Glory Let Us Sing!" (31).

42 Jesus, the Very Thought of You

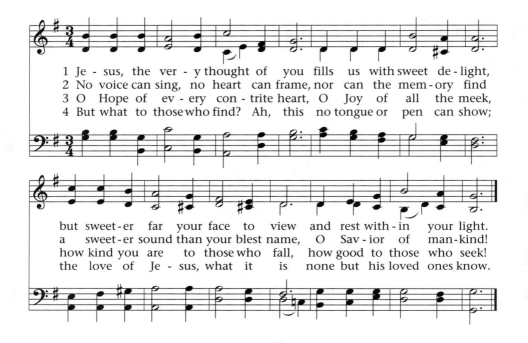

1 Je - sus, the ver - y thought of you fills us with sweet de - light,
2 No voice can sing, no heart can frame, nor can the mem - ory find
3 O Hope of ev - ery con - trite heart, O Joy of all the meek,
4 But what to those who find? Ah, this no tongue or pen can show;

but sweet - er far your face to view and rest with - in your light.
a sweet - er sound than your blest name, O Sav - ior of man - kind!
how kind you are to those who fall, how good to those who seek!
the love of Je - sus, what it is none but his loved ones know.

Words: Latin (ca. 1150); tr. Edward Caswall (1849), alt., P.D.
Music: John B. Dykes (1866), P.D.

86 86
ST. AGNES

The long Latin poem "Jesu Dulcis Memoria," attributed (without proof) to the mystic Bernard of Clairvaux, comes from the medieval tradition of monastic writings for personal devotion. It helps us express a passionate devotion to Christ and be in awe of his love. Dykes composed an unassuming melody for this text, resulting in a union of text and music that still appears in some modern hymnals.

Good Christian Friends, Rejoice   43

1 Good Chris-tian friends, re - joice   with heart and soul and voice;
2 Good Chris-tian friends, re - joice   with heart and soul and voice;
3 Good Chris-tian friends, re - joice   with heart and soul and voice;

give   ye heed   to what we   say: Je - sus Christ   is   born   to-day.
now   ye hear   of   end-less bliss: Je - sus Christ was born   for this!
now   ye need   not fear the grave: Je - sus Christ was born   to save!

Ox   and ass be - fore him bow, and he   is   in   the man-ger now.
He   has o-pened heav-en's door, and we   are blest   for - ev - er-more.
Calls you one and   calls you   all   to gain his ev - er - last-ing hall.

Christ   is   born   to - day!   Christ   is   born   to - day!
Christ   was born   for   this!   Christ   was born   for   this!
Christ   was born   to   save!   Christ   was born   to   save!

Words: Latin-German (ca. 1340); tr. John M. Neale (1853), alt., P.D.   66 77 78 55
Music: German (14th cent.), P.D.   IN DULCI JUBILO

This is the best-known example of a macaronic carol (a folk text in several languages), in this case with alternating
Latin and German phrases beginning: "In dulci jubilo, nun singet und seit froh." The joy of this text is well supported by the rhythmic energy of the folk dance melody.

44 Come Down, O Love Divine

1 Come down, O Love divine; seek thou this soul of mine,
2 O let it freely burn, till earthly passions turn
3 Let holy charity mine outward vesture be,
4 And so the yearning strong, with which the soul will long,

and visit it with thine own ardor glowing.
to dust and ashes in its heat consuming;
and lowliness become mine inner clothing—
shall far outpass the power of human telling;

O Comforter, draw near; within my heart appear
and let thy glorious light shine ever on my sight,
true lowliness of heart, which takes the humbler part,
no soul can guess his grace till it become the place

and kindle it, thy holy flame bestowing.
and clothe me round, the while my path illuming.
and o'er its own shortcomings weeps with loathing.
wherein the Holy Spirit makes his dwelling.

Words: Bianco da Siena (ca. 1350-1434); tr. Richard F. Littledale (1867), P.D.
Music: Ralph Vaughan Williams (1906), P.D.

66 11 66 11
DOWN AMPNEY

This sung prayer for the Holy Spirit is from the genre of *laudi spirituali*—unofficial vernacular hymns of devotion that developed in Italian Roman Catholicism in the thirteenth and fourteenth centuries. Vaughan Williams composed his distinguished tune for use in the *English Hymnal* with this text.

O Sons and Daughters 45

Alleluia, alleluia, alleluia, alleluia!

1 O sons and daugh-ters of the King, whom heav-enly hosts in
2 That Eas-ter morn at break of day, the faith-ful wom-en
3 An an-gel clad in white they see, who sat and spoke un-
4 When Thom-as first the tid-ings heard that some had seen the

Final time D.S. al Fine

glo-ry sing, to-day the grave has lost its sting. Al-le-lu-ia!
went their way to seek the tomb where Je-sus lay. Al-le-lu-ia!
to the three,"Your Lord has gone to Gal-i-lee." Al-le-lu-ia!
ris-en Lord, he doubt-ed the dis-ci-ples' word. Lord, have mer-cy!

5 At night the apostles met in fear;
among them came their Master dear
and said, "My peace be with you here."
Alleluia!

6 "My pierced side, O Thomas, see,
and look upon my hands, my feet;
not faithless but believing be."
Alleluia!

7 No longer Thomas then denied;
he saw the feet, the hands, the side.
"You are my Lord and God!" he cried.
Alleluia!

8 How blest are they who have not seen
and yet whose faith has constant been,
for they eternal life shall win.
Alleluia!

Words: Jean Tisserand (1494); tr. John M. Neale (1851), alt., P.D.
Music: *Airs sur les hymnes sacrez, odes et noëls*, Paris (1623), P.D.

888 with alleluias
O FILII ET FILIAE

Unusual for Easter hymns, this is a narrative text that combines Matthew 28:1-10 and John 20:19-29. Originally in Latin, several stanzas were added to Tisserand's text and surrounded by opening and closing "alleluias." Though not published until 1623, the tune is thought to be contemporaneous with the text.

46　O Love, How Deep, How Broad, How High

Unison

1 O love, how deep; how broad, how high, be - yond all
2 For us bap - tized, for us he bore his ho - ly
3 For us he prayed; for us he taught; for us his
4 For us to e - vil power be - trayed, scourged, mocked, in

thought and fan - ta - sy, that God, the Son of
fast and hun - gered sore; for us temp - ta - tion
dai - ly works he wrought: by words and signs and
pur - ple robe ar - rayed, he bore the shame - ful

God, should take our mor - tal form for mor - tals' sake!
sharp he knew, for us the tempt - er o - ver - threw.
ac - tions thus still seek - ing not him - self, but us.
cross and death; for us gave up his dy - ing breath.

5 For us he rose from death again;
   for us he went on high to reign;
   for us he sent his Spirit here
   to guide, to strengthen, and to cheer.

6 All glory to our Lord and God
   for love so deep, so high, so broad—
   the Trinity, whom we adore
   forever and forevermore.

Words: Latin, "O Amor Quam Ecstaticus" (15th c.); tr. Benjamin Webb (1854), alt., P.D.　　　　88 88
Music: English (15th c.); harm. Carl Schalk (1969) © 1969 Concordia Publishing House.　　DEO GRACIAS
　　Used by permission.

This text has a wide scope, treating Jesus' life, death, resurrection, and coming again much as the Apostles' Creed treats them. The rhythmically vigorous tune for these words, originally associated with a ballad about the Battle of Agincourt, is a fine match for this text, and first became a hymn-tune in the *English Hymnal* (1906).

Christ Jesus Lay in Death's Strong Bonds 47

1 Christ Je - sus lay in death's strong bands, for our of - fens - es
2 It was a strange and dread - ful strife when life and death con -
3 Here the true pas - chal Lamb we see, whom God so free - ly

giv - en; but now at God's right hand he stands and brings us life
tend - ed. The vic - to - ry re - mained with life; the reign of death
gave us. He died on the ac - curs - ed tree— so strong his love—

from heav - en. There-fore let us joy - ful be, and sing to God
was end - ed. Ho - ly Scrip-ture plain - ly says his death has swal -
to save us. See, his blood now marks our door; faith points to it,

right thank-ful - ly loud songs of al - le - lu - ia! Al-le - lu - ia!
lowed up our death; its sting is lost for - ev - er. Al-le - lu - ia!
death pass - es o'er, and Sa - tan can - not harm us. Al-le - lu - ia!

4 So let us keep the festival
  to which the Lord invites us.
Christ is himself the joy of all,
  the sun that warms and lights us.
Now his grace to us imparts
  eternal sunshine to our hearts;
the night of sin is ended. Alleluia!

5 Then let us feast this holy day
  on Christ, the bread of heaven.
The Word of grace has purged away
  the old and evil leaven.
Christ alone our souls will feed;
  he is our meat and drink indeed;
faith lives upon no other! Alleluia!

Words: Martin Luther (1524); tr. Richard Massie (1854), alt., P.D.
Music: J. Walther's *Geystliche Gesang Buchlein* (1524), P.D.

87 87 78 74
CHRIST LAG IN TODESBANDEN

Luther wrote this text to "improve" on an older German Easter hymn, "Christ Ist Erstanden," which in itself was based on an even older Latin hymn, "Victimae Paschali Laudes." The ending "alleluia" phrase was originally "Kyrie eleison," a common feature of medieval hymns in Germany which were collectively known as *leisen*.

48 A Mighty Fortress Is Our God

1 A might-y for-tress is our God, a bul-wark
2 Did we in our own strength con-fide, our striv-ing
3 And though this world, with dev-ils filled, should threat-en
4 That Word a-bove all earth-ly powers— no thanks to

nev-er fail-ing; Our help-er he, a-mid the flood
would be los-ing, were not the right Man on our side,
to un-do us, we will not fear, for God has willed
them— a-bid-eth; the Spir-it and the gifts are ours

of mor-tal ills pre-vail-ing. For still our an-cient foe
the Man of God's own choos-ing. You ask who that may be?
his truth to tri-umph through us. The prince of dark-ness grim,
through him who with us sid-eth. Let goods and kin-dred go,

does seek to work us woe; his craft and power are great,
Christ Je-sus, it is he; Lord Sa-ba-oth his name,
we trem-ble not for him; his rage we can en-dure,
this mor-tal life al-so; the bod-y they may kill:

Words: Martin Luther (1529); tr. Frederick H. Hedge (1852); based on Psalm 46, P.D.
Music: Martin Luther (1529), alt.; harm. Johann S. Bach (ca. 1728), P.D.

87 87 66 66 7
EIN FESTE BURG

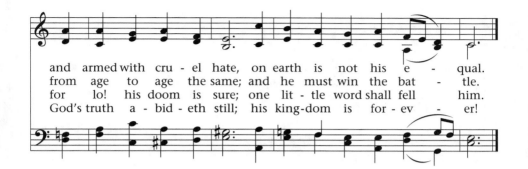

and armed with cru - el hate, on earth is not his e - qual.
from age to age the same; and he must win the bat - tle.
for lo! his doom is sure; one lit - tle word shall fell him.
God's truth a - bid - eth still; his king-dom is for - ev - er!

This hymn by Luther became one of the great "battle cry" songs of the Protestant Reformation, but even today it is much loved by both Protestants and Roman Catholics for its conviction that "God's truth abides" against all powers of evil. Luther originally composed the tune in lively rhythms, but the isorhythmic setting (in equal quarter notes, with Bach's interesting harmony) has gained popularity.

49 From Heaven Above to Earth I Come

1 "From heaven a-bove to earth I come to bring good
2 "To you this night is born a child of Mar - y,
3 "This is the Christ, God's Son most high, who hears your
4 "These are the signs which you shall mark: the swad - dling

news to ev - ery home! Glad tid - ings of great
cho - sen vir - gin mild; this lit - tle child of
sad and bit - ter cry; he will him - self your
clothes and man - ger dark. There you shall find the

joy I bring to all the world, and glad - ly sing:
low - ly birth shall be the joy of all the earth.
Sav - ior be, from all your sins to set you free.
in - fant laid by whom the heavens and earth were made."

5 We too must join the angel throng
to sing again this joyful song:
"All glory be to God in heaven,
who unto us his Son has given."

Words: Martin Luther (1535); tr. composite; based on Luke 2:10-14, P.D.   88 88
Music: Valentin Schumann's *Geistliche Lieder* (1539), P.D.   VOM HIMMEL HOCH

Originally in 15 stanzas, Luther penned this narrative text and spritely tune for Christmas Eve table devotions on
Luke 2, intending that stanzas 1-7 be sung by a man dressed as an angel and stanzas 8-15 by children. The stanzas
selected here focus on the angels' message as presented in Luke 2:10-14.

I Greet My Sure Redeemer 50

1 I greet my sure Re-deem-er and my King. You are my
2 You are the King of mer-cy and of grace, reign-ing om-
3 You are the life by which a-lone we live and all our
4 You have the true and per-fect gen - tle - ness. You have no

trust; ac-cept the love I bring. What pain you suf-fered, Je - sus,
nip - o - tent in ev - ery place; so come, O King, and our whole
sub - stance and our strength re - ceive. Sus - tain us by your faith and
harsh-ness and no bit - ter-ness. Lord, grant to us the grace in

for my sake; I pray you from our hearts all cares to take.
be - ing sway; shine on us with the light of your pure day.
by your power, and give us strength in ev - ery try - ing hour.
you we see that we may live in per - fect u - ni - ty.

5 Our hope is founded on your holy Word.
Our faith is built on every promise, Lord.
Grant us your peace; make us so strong and pure
that we may conquerors be, all ills endure.

Words: French "Je te salve, mon certain Redempteur" (1545); tr. Elizabeth L. Smith (1868), alt., P.D.   10 10 10 10
Music: Louis Bourgeois (1551), harm. after Claude Goudimel (1564), P.D.   JE TU SALUE

Sometimes erroneously attributed to John Calvin, this text is a Protestant adaptation of the Roman Catholic hymn "Salve Regina." The melody, later altered by an unknown hand, was originally composed by Bourgeois for use with Psalm 101 in the Genevan Psalter.

51 In You Is Gladness

1 In you is glad-ness a-mid all sad-ness, Je - sus, sun - shine
2 If he is ours, _____ we fear no pow-ers— not of sin or

of my heart. By you are giv - en the gifts of heav - en;
death or night. He knows our trou - bles, our pain and strug - gles;

you the true Re - deem - er are. Our hearts you wak - en,
he up - holds us by his might. Where-fore the sto - ry—

we're not for - sak - en; who trusts you sure - ly has built se -
tell of his glo - ry with heart and voic - es; all heaven re -

cure-ly and stands for - ev - er: Al - le - lu - ia! Our hearts are
joic - es in him for - ev - er: Al - le - lu - ia! We shout for

Words: Johann Lindemann (1598); tr. Catherine Winkworth (1858), alt., P.D.
Music: Giovanni G. Gastoldi (1591), P.D.

557D 55554D
IN DIR IST FREUDE

Built with short biblical phrases and allusions, this text confesses with joyful alleluias the Christian's security and comfort of walking intimately with God. The music is light-hearted dance music composed with various repeats in the melody; it calls for long phrases rather than short choppy phrases.

52 Wake, Awake, for Night Is Flying

1 Wake, a-wake, for night is fly - ing, the watch-men on the
2 Zi - on hears the watch-men sing - ing, and all her heart with
3 Glo - ri - a! Let heaven a-dore you! Let saints and an - gels

heights are cry - ing; a - wake, Je - ru - sa - lem, at last.
joy is spring - ing. She wakes, she ris - es from her gloom.
sing be - fore you, with harp and cym-bal's clear-est tone.

Mid-night hears the wel-come voic - es, and at the thrill-ing
Her dear friend comes down, all glo - rious, the strong in grace, in
Gates of pearl, twelve por - tals gleam - ing, lead us to bliss be-

cry re - joic - es: "Come forth, you maid-ens! Night is past.
truth vic - to - rious: her star is risen; her light is come.
yond all dream - ing, with an - gel choirs a - round your throne.

Words: Philipp Nicolai (1599); tr. composite © 1999 Augsburg Fortress
Music: Hans Sachs (ca. 1513); adapt. Philipp Nicolai (1599), P.D.

898 898 66 4 88
WACHET AUF [RHYTHMIC]

The bride-groom comes! A - wake; your lamps with glad - ness take!"
Now come, O Bless - ed One, Lord Je - sus, God's own Son.
No eye has caught the light, no ear the thun-dering might

Al - le - lu - ia! Rise and pre-pare the feast to share;
Sing ho - san - na! Oh, hear the call! Come one, come all,
of such glo - ry. There we will go; what joy we'll know!

go, meet the bride-groom, who draws near.
and fol - low to the ban - quet hall.
There sweet de - light will ev - er flow.

Written amid the ravages of a terrible pestilence in his village, Nicolai's Advent text was inspired by Jesus' parable of the ten virgins (Matt. 25:1-13) and John's vision of Christ's glory in the new Jerusalem (Rev. 19, 21, and 22). Nicolai adapted a Meistersinger melody for his words, given here in its rhythmic form (as opposed to Bach's harmonization in isorhythm—all equal quarter notes—which is found in some hymnals).

53 Lo, How a Rose E'er Blooming

1 Lo, how a rose e'er bloom-ing from ten-der stem hath
2 I - sa - iah 'twas fore-told it, the rose I have in
3 This flower, so small and ten-der, with fra-grance fills the

sprung; of Jes - se's lin-eage com-ing, as saints of old have
mind; with Mar - y we be-hold it, the vir - gin moth - er
air; his bright-ness ends the dark-ness that kept the earth in

sung. It came, a flower - et bright, a - mid the
kind. To show God's love a - right she bore to
fear. True God and yet true man, he came to

cold of win - ter when half spent was the night.
us a Sav - ior when half spent was the night.
save his peo - ple from earth's dark night of sin.

Words: German (15th c.).; st. 1-2 tr. Theodore Baker (1894); st. 3 tr. Gracia Grindal (1978)   76 76 676
© 1978 Lutheran Book of Worship. Used by permission of Augsburg Publishing House.
Music: *Alte Catholische Geistliche Kirchengesäng*, Cologne (1599);   ES IST EIN' ROS' ENTSPRUNGEN
    harm. Michael Praetorius (1609), P.D.

This was originally a German "Twelfth Night" carol with a stanza that interpreted the rose as Mary, but by the time the Lutheran Praetorius published the text and melody in his *Musae Sionae* (1609), the rose was now Christ, in accord with Isaiah 11:1. That folk melody appeared in a Roman Catholic songbook; its madrigal character invites unaccompanied singing. Another text with this tune is "A Great and Mighty Wonder" (30).

We Gather Together 54

1 We gath - er to - geth - er to ask the Lord's bless - ing;
2 Be - side us to guide us, our God with us join - ing,
3 We all do ex - tol thee, our lead - er tri - um - phant,

he chas - tens and has - tens his will to make known.
or - dain - ing, main - tain - ing his king - dom di - vine;
and pray that thou still our de - fend - er wilt be;

The wick - ed op - press - ing now cease from dis - tress - ing;
so from the be - gin - ning the fight we were win - ning.
let thy con - gre - ga - tion es - cape trib - u - la - tion.

sing prais - es to his name: he for - gets not his own.
Thou, Lord, wast at our side, all glo - ry be thine!
Thy name be ev - er praised! O Lord, make us free!

Words: Dutch, "Wilt Heden Nu Treden" (16th c.); tr. Theodore Baker (1917), P.D.
Music: Adrianus Valerius' *Nederlandtsch Gedenckclanck* (1626); arr. Edward Kremser (1877), P.D.

12 11 12 11
KREMSER

This anonymous patriotic Dutch text appeared after Holland gained its freedom from Spanish rule. Edward Kremser discovered this song in Valerius' collection and published it with five others in 1877. That led to Baker's translation of these words into English, and the use of this hymn as a prayer for God's providence to prevail in our lives.

55 Ah, Holy Jesus, How Have You Offended

1 Ah, holy Jesus, how have you offended,
that mortal judgment has on you descended? By foes derided, by your own rejected, O most afflicted!

2 Who was the guilty? Who brought this upon you?
It is my treason, Lord, that has undone you. 'Twas I, Lord Jesus, I it was denied you; I crucified you.

3 For me, dear Jesus, was your incarnation,
your mortal sorrow, and your life's oblation; your death of anguish and your bitter passion, for my salvation.

4 Therefore, dear Jesus, since I cannot pay you,
I do adore you and will ever pray you, think on your pity and your love unswerving, not my deserving.

Words: Johann Heermann (1630); tr. Robert Bridges (1899), alt., P.D.
Music: Johann Crüger (1640), P.D.

11 11 11 5
HERZLIEBSTER JESU

Heermann's text was written during the agonies of the Thirty Years' War. It was translated later by Bridges and published in his *Yattendon Hymnal* (1899). A deeply personal testimony by a Lutheran pastor—"I it was denied you; I crucified you"—this hymn is our Christian corporate witness to Christ's atonement.

Come, My Way, My Truth, My Life   56

Unison

1 Come, my Way, my Truth, my Life: such a
2 Come, my Light, my Feast, my Strength: such a
3 Come, my Joy, my Love, my Heart: such a

way as gives us breath, such a truth as ends all
light as shows a feast, such a feast as mends in
joy as none can move, such a love as none can

strife, such a life as kill - eth death.
length, such a strength as makes his guest.
part, such a heart as joys in love.

Words: George Herbert (1633), P.D.   77 77
Music: Ralph Vaughan Williams (1911); adapt. E. Harold Geer (1956) © Stainer & Bell Ltd.   THE CALL

Not intended originally for singing, this text is rich in biblical imagery and paradox that would merit some study
or commentary for any congregation that does sing it. Vaughan Williams set this text as the fourth of his *Five
Mystical Songs* for baritone solo, chorus, and orchestra.

57 Let All the World

Unison

1 Let all the world in ev-ery cor-ner sing: my God and King!
2 Let all the world in ev-ery cor-ner sing: my God and King!

The heavens are not too high, his praise may thi - ther fly;
The church with psalms must shout, no door can keep them out;

the earth is not too low, his prais - es there may grow.
but, more than all, the heart must bear the long - est part.

Let all the world in ev-ery cor-ner sing: my God and King!
Let all the world in ev-ery cor-ner sing: my God and King!

Words: George Herbert (1633), P.D.
Music: Paul Liljestrand, © 1970 The Hymn Society (Admin.Hope Publishing Company)

14 12 12 14
CONRAD

Featuring an antiphon (refrain) in his text, Herbert calls us to join with, and testify to, the whole world that God is our King. Liljestrand's tune was originally composed for Bryan J. Leech's text, "Through All the World Let Every Nation Sing," which was modeled directly on Herbert's poem.

Now Thank We All Our God 58

1 Now thank we all our God with heart and hands and voic - es,
2 O may this boun-teous God through all our life be near us,
3 All praise and thanks to God the Fa - ther now be giv - en,

who won-drous things has done, in whom his world re - joic - es;
with ev - er joy - ful hearts and bless - ed peace to cheer us,
the Son and Spir - it blest, who reign in high-est heav - en—

who from our moth-ers' arms has blessed us on our way
to keep us in his grace, and guide us when per - plexed,
the one e - ter - nal God, whom heaven and earth a - dore;

with count-less gifts of love, and still is ours to - day.
and free us from all ills of this world in the next.
for thus it was, is now, and shall be ev - er - more.

Words: Martin Rinkart (1636); tr. Catherine Winkworth (1863), alt., P.D.   67 67 66 66
Music: Johann Crüger (1647); harm. based on Felix Mendelssohn's *Lobgesang*, Opus 52 (1840), P.D.   NUN DANKET

A Lutheran pastor in Eilenburg, Germany, Rinkart (also spelled Rinkhart) wrote this famous text amid the horrors of the Thirty Years War, which inspired in him sacrificial service and the writing of hymns of praise and confidence in God. Crüger's melody is here given in its isorhythmic form (equal quarter notes), for which the dramatic harmonization by Mendelssohn (from his *Symphony No. 2*) is a fortunate complement.

59 Clothe Yourself, My Soul, with Gladness

1 Clothe your-self, my soul, with glad-ness, leave the gloom-y
2 Has-ten as a bride to meet him, and with lov-ing
3 How we long with all our spir-it for the love we
4 Je-sus, bread of life, we pray you, let us glad-ly

haunts of sad-ness. Come in-to the day-light's splen-dor,
rev-erence greet him; for with words of love and mer-cy
do not mer-it. From our wea-ry sighs, Lord, free us,
here o-bey you. By this ban-quet let us mea-sure,

there with joy your prais-es ren-der. Praise the Lord,
Christ is knock-ing, seek-ing en-try. O-pen wide
with this heav-enly food now feed us. May we, when
Lord, how vast your love, our trea-sure. By your grace

whose grace un-bound-ed has this won-drous ban-quet
the gates be-fore him; kneel-ing at his feet, a-
by life dis-cour-aged, by this cup of life be
we are in-vit-ed, by your love we are u-

Words: Johann Franck (1649); tr. Catherine Winkworth (1863); rev. *Psalter Hymnal,*
1987 © 1987 Faith Alive Christian Resources
Music: Johann Crüger (1649), P.D.

88 88 D

SCHMÜCKE DICH

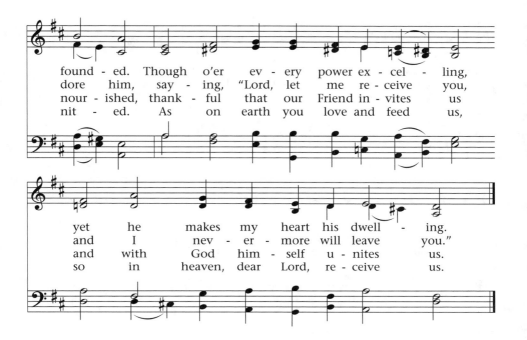

found - ed. Though o'er ev - ery power ex - cel - ling,
dore him, say - ing, "Lord, let me re - ceive you,
nour - ished, thank - ful that our Friend in - vites us
nit - ed. As on earth you love and feed us,

yet he makes my heart his dwell - ing.
and I nev - er - more will leave you."
and with God him - self u - nites us.
so in heaven, dear Lord, re - ceive us.

Thought to be among the finest of the Lutheran chorales for the Lord's Supper, this text expresses a profound joy and awe for Christ's gift of "this wondrous banquet." It is made even more eloquent by the rhythmic interest of the dance-like tune. What a delight: dance music for the Lord's Supper!

60　If You But Trust in God to Guide You

1 If you but trust in God to guide you and place your con-fi-
2 On-ly be still and wait his plea-sure in cheer-ful hope with
3 Sing, pray, and keep his ways un-swerv-ing, of-fer your ser-vice

dence in him, you'll find him al-ways there be-side you
heart con-tent. He fills your needs to full-est mea-sure
faith-ful-ly, and trust his word; though un-de-serv-ing,

to give you hope and strength with-in; for those who trust God's
with what dis-cern-ing love has sent; doubt not our in-most
you'll find his prom-ise true to be. God nev-er will for-

change-less love build on the rock that will not move.
wants are known to him who chose us for his own.
sake in need the soul that trusts in him in-deed.

Words: Georg Neumark (1641); tr. composite, P.D.　　　　　　　　　　　　　　98 98 88
Music: Georg Neumark (1657), P.D.　　　　　　　　　　　　　WER NUR DEN LIEBEN GOTT

Neumark wrote this text in thanksgiving to God for providing employment, but its confession of confidence in God's providence is also inspired by his experience of God's care during the difficult time of the Thirty Years War. Neumark later composed a tune for his text, and his hymn is much loved in various Christian traditions. The English translation is much revised from that prepared by Catherine Winkworth in her *Chorale Book for England* (1863).

Jesus, Priceless Treasure 61

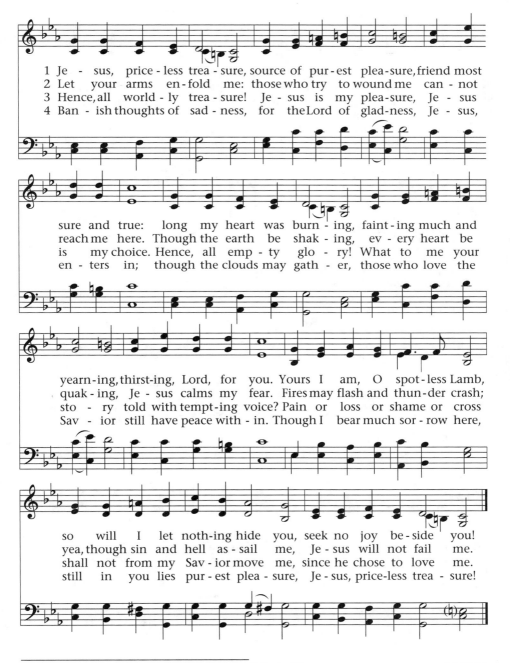

1 Je - sus, price-less trea-sure, source of pur-est plea-sure, friend most
2 Let your arms en-fold me: those who try to wound me can-not
3 Hence, all world-ly trea-sure! Je - sus is my plea-sure, Je - sus
4 Ban - ish thoughts of sad-ness, for the Lord of glad-ness, Je - sus,

sure and true: long my heart was burn - ing, faint-ing much and
reach me here. Though the earth be shak - ing, ev - ery heart be
is my choice. Hence, all emp-ty glo - ry! What to me your
en - ters in; though the clouds may gath - er, those who love the

yearn-ing, thirst-ing, Lord, for you. Yours I am, O spot-less Lamb,
quak - ing, Je - sus calms my fear. Fires may flash and thun-der crash;
sto - ry told with tempt-ing voice? Pain or loss or shame or cross
Sav - ior still have peace with - in. Though I bear much sor - row here,

so will I let noth-ing hide you, seek no joy be-side you!
yea, though sin and hell as-sail me, Je - sus will not fail me.
shall not from my Sav-ior move me, since he chose to love me.
still in you lies pur-est plea-sure, Je - sus, price-less trea-sure!

Words: Johann Franck (1653); tr. Catherine Winkworth (1863), alt., P.D.
Music: Johann Crüger (1653), P.D.

665 665 786
JESU, MEINE FREUDE

Modeled after a German love song, this chorale helps us focus on Jesus as the greatest treasure in our lives. Its language is rich in biblical allusions and deeply emotional. Johann S. Bach composed various harmonizations and elaborations of this tune; one of these is provided here in simpler form.

62 Christ, the Life of All the Living

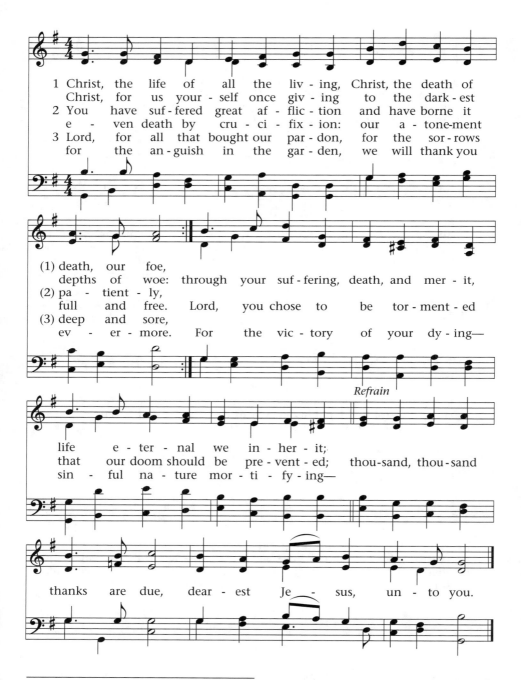

1 Christ, the life of all the liv - ing, Christ, the death of
Christ, for us your - self once giv - ing to the dark - est
2 You have suf - fered great af - flic - tion and have borne it
e - ven death by cru - ci - fix - ion: our a - tone-ment
3 Lord, for all that bought our par - don, for the sor - rows
for the an - guish in the gar - den, we will thank you

(1) death, our foe,
depths of woe: through your suf - fering, death, and mer - it,
(2) pa - tient - ly,
full and free. Lord, you chose to be tor - ment - ed
(3) deep and sore,
ev - er - more. For the vic - tory of your dy - ing—

Refrain

life e - ter - nal we in - her - it;
that our doom should be pre - vent - ed; thou-sand, thou-sand
sin - ful na - ture mor - ti - fy - ing—

thanks are due, dear - est Je - sus, un - to you.

Words: Ernst C. Homburg (1659); tr. Catherine Winkworth (1863), alt., P.D.   87 87 with refrain
Music: *Das grosse Cantionale*, Darmstadt (1687), P.D.   JESU, MEINES LEBEN'S LEBEN

Set to a chorale melody with some rhythmic interest, this text is a Lenten meditation on the suffering and death of
Christ in which each stanza leads to gratitude: "thousand, thousand thanks are due, dearest Jesus, unto you."

Blessed Jesus, at Your Word 63

1 Bless - ed Je - sus, at your word we are gath - ered
2 All our knowl-edge, sense, and sight lie in deep - est
3 Glo - rious Lord, your - self im - part; Light of Light, from

all to hear you. Let our hearts and souls be stirred
dark-ness shroud - ed, till your Spir - it breaks our night
God pro - ceed - ing, o - pen lips and ears and heart;

now to seek and love and fear you. By your gos - pel
with your beams of truth un - cloud - ed. You a - lone to
help us by your Spir - it's lead - ing. Hear the cry your

pure and ho - ly, teach us, Lord, to love you sole - ly.
God can win us; you must work all good with - in us.
church now rais - es; Lord, ac - cept our prayers and prais - es.

Words: Tobias Clausnitzer (1663); tr. Catherine Winkworth (1858), alt., P.D.   78 78 88
Music: Johann R. Ahle (1664), P.D.   LIEBSTER JESU

This is a sung prayer for illumination asking the Holy Spirit to stir our hearts to receive the Word that is to be read and preached. The serene chorale melody comes from Ahle's collection of "sacred arias."

64 My Song Is Love Unknown

1 My song is love un-known, my Sav-ior's love to me.
2 Christ came from his blest throne sal - va - tion to be - stow;
3 Some-times we strew his way, and his sweet prais - es sing,

Love to the love-less shown, that they might love - ly be.
the world that was his own would not its Sav - ior know.
re - sound-ing all the day ho - san - nas to the King.

O who am I, that for my sake
But, O my friend, my friend in - deed,
Then "Cru - ci - fy!" is all our breath,

my Lord should take frail flesh, and die?
who at my need his life did spend!
and for his death we thirst and cry.

4 We hear the shouts that have
our dear Lord done away;
a murderer they save,
the Prince of life they slay.
Yet cheerful he to suffering goes
that he his foes from thence might free.

5 Here might I stay and sing,
no story so divine;
never was love, dear King,
never was grief like thine!
This is my friend, in whose sweet praise
I all my days could gladly spend!

Words: Samuel Crossman (1664), alt., P.D.
Music: John N. Ireland (1919) © 1924 John Ireland
(admin. by The John Ireland Trust)

66 66 44 44
LOVE UNKNOWN

One of nine poems that Crossman published in a pamphlet, this text is a sung sermon on Jesus' atonement, made deeply personal by the claim that Christ "is my friend." Ireland's melody, with its delightful rhythms that shift between duple and triple, was composed for this text, giving Crossman's words new life in modern hymnody.

Comfort, Comfort Now My People   65

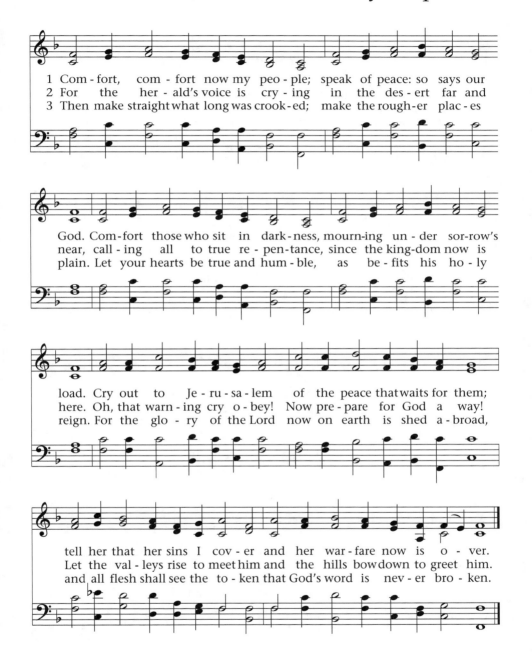

1 Com - fort,   com - fort now my peo - ple;   speak of peace: so   says our
2 For   the   her - ald's voice is   cry - ing   in   the des - ert   far and
3 Then make straight what long was crook - ed;   make the rough - er   plac - es

God. Com - fort those who sit   in   dark - ness, mourn - ing un - der sor - row's
near, call - ing   all   to true re - pen - tance, since the king - dom now is
plain. Let   your hearts be true and hum - ble,   as   be - fits his ho - ly

load. Cry out   to   Je - ru - sa - lem   of   the peace that waits for them;
here. Oh, that warn - ing cry o - bey!   Now pre - pare for God   a   way!
reign. For the   glo - ry   of the Lord   now on earth   is shed a - broad,

tell her that her sins I   cov - er and her   war - fare now is   o - ver.
Let the val - leys rise to meet him and   the   hills bow down to greet him.
and all flesh shall see the to - ken that God's word is   nev - er bro - ken.

Words: Isaiah 40:1-5; vers. Johannes G. Olearius (1671); tr. Catherine Winkworth (1863), alt., P.D.   87 87 77 88
Music: Louis Bourgeois (1551); harm. Claude Goudimel (1564), P.D.   GENEVAN 42

This biblical text opens the second section of prophecies by Isaiah (ch. 40-66), which is characterized by offers of consolation and further calls to repentance. Bourgeois composed this melody for use with Psalm 42 in the Genevan Psalter; in German hymnody this tune is known as FREU DICH SEHR.

66 Sing Praise to God Who Reigns Above

1 Sing praise to God who reigns a-bove, the God of all
2 What God's al-might-y power has made, in mer-cy he
3 We sought the Lord in our dis-tress; O God, in mer-
4 Let all who name Christ's ho-ly name give God the praise

cre-a-tion, the God of power, the God of love, the
is keep-ing; by morn-ing glow or eve-ning shade his
cy hear us. Our Sav-ior saw our help-less-ness and
and glo-ry. Let all who know his power pro-claim a-

God of our sal-va-tion. My soul with com-fort rich he fills,
eye is nev-er sleep-ing. And where he rules in king-ly might,
came with peace to cheer us. For this we thank and praise the Lord,
loud the won-drous sto-ry. Cast ev-ery i-dol from its throne;

and ev-ery grief he gent-ly stills: to God all praise and glo-ry!
there all is just and all is right: to God all praise and glo-ry!
who is by one and all a-dored: to God all praise and glo-ry!
the Lord is God, and he a-lone: to God all praise and glo-ry!

Words: Johann J. Schütz (1675); tr. Frances Cox (1864), alt., P.D.
Music: Bohemian Brethren's *Kirchengesänge* (1566); harm. Heinrich Reimann (1895), P.D.

87 87 887
MIT FREUDEN ZART

A Pietist who eventually left the Lutheran Church to become a Moravian, Schütz wrote this "Hymn of Thanksgiving" in the style of the Old Testament praise psalms. The melody comes from an early tune-book in the Moravian tradition and bears resemblance to the Genevan tune for Psalm 138. This music is also used with "God Has Gone Up with Shouts of Joy!" (252).

Beautiful Savior   67

1 Beau - ti - ful Sav - ior! King of cre - a - tion!
2 Fair are the mead - ows, fair are the wood - lands,
3 Fair is the sun - shine, fair is the moon - light,
4 Beau - ti - ful Sav - ior! Lord of the na - tions!

Son of God and Son of Man!
robed in flowers of bloom - ing spring;
bright the spar - kling stars on high;
Son of God and Son of Man!

Tru - ly I'd love thee, tru - ly I'd serve thee,
Je - sus is fair - er, Je - sus is pur - er;
Je - sus shines bright - er, Je - sus shines pur - er
Glo - ry and hon - or, praise, ad - o - ra - tion,

Light of my soul, my joy, my crown.
he makes our sor - rowing spir - it sing.
than all the an - gels in the sky.
now and for - ev - er - more be thine!

Words: *Gesangbuch*, Münster (1677); tr. Joseph A. Seiss (1873), P.D.   557 558
Music: *Schleisische Volkslieder* (1842), P.D.   ST. ELIZABETH

Expressing love and praise for Christ, the King of creation and the Lord of the nations, this text is set to a Silesian melody which, legend has it, was sung by the crusaders during the twelfth century, and which Franz Liszt incorporated in his oratorio *The Legend of St. Elizabeth* (1862).

68 God, My Hope on You Is Founded

1 God, my hope on you is found-ed; you my faith and trust re-new: through all change and chance you guide me, on-ly good and on-ly true. God un-known, you a-lone call my heart to be your own.

2 Hu-man pride and earth-ly glo-ry, sword and crown be-tray our trust; though with care and toil we build them, tower and tem-ple fall to dust. But your power, hour by hour, is my tem-ple and my tower.

3 Dai-ly does the al-might-y Giv-er boun-teous gifts on us be-stow; God's de-sire for us de-lights us, plea-sure leads us where we go. Here at hand, love takes stand, joy a-waits God's sure com-mand.

Words: Joachim Neander (1680); tr. Robert Seymour Bridges (1898), alt., P.D.
Music: Herbert Howells (1930) © Novello & Co., Ltd. Reprinted by permission
of Shawnee Press, Inc. (ASCAP).

87 87 337
MICHAEL

4 God's great goodness lasts forever,
   deepest wisdom, passing thought:
   splendor, light, and life attending,
   beauty springing out of naught.
   Evermore from God's store
   newborn worlds rise and adore.

5 Still from earth to God eternal
   sacrifice of praise be done,
   high above all praises praising
   for the gift of Christ the Son.
   Christ, you call one and all;
   those who follow shall not fall.

The German Reformed Pietist Neander entitled this text "Grace After Meat." Bridges prepared the very free translation for his *Yattendon Hymnal* (1899), while the British composer Howells actually wrote this grand tune for this text "during breakfast," naming it after his son.

69 Praise to the Lord, the Almighty

1 Praise to the Lord, the Al-might-y, the King of cre-a-tion! O my soul, praise him, for he is your health and sal-va-tion! Come, all who hear; broth-ers and sis-ters, draw near, join me in glad ad-o-ra-tion!

2 Praise to the Lord, who o'er all things is won-drous-ly reign-ing, shel-tering you un-der his wings, oh, so gent-ly sus-tain-ing. Have you not seen all that is need-ful has been sent by his gra-cious or-dain-ing?

3 Praise to the Lord, who will pros-per your work and de-fend you; sure-ly his good-ness and mer-cy shall dai-ly at-tend you. Pon-der a-new what the Al-might-y can do as with his love he be-friends you.

4 Praise to the Lord! O let all that is in me a-dore him! All that has life and breath, come now with prais-es be-fore him! Let the a-men sound from his peo-ple a-gain. Glad-ly for-ev-er a-dore him!

Words: Joachim Neander (1680); tr. Catherine Winkworth (1863), alt., P.D.
Music: *Ernewerten Gesangbuch*, Stralsund, 1665, P.D.

14 14 478
LOBE DEN HERREN

Loosely based on Psalm 103:1-6 and filled with echoes of other psalms, Neander's text is one of the great praise hymns in the Lutheran tradition, ably supported by one of the finest Lutheran chorale melodies. Note the long opening phrases, followed by shorter phrases, the first of which contains the well-positioned climactic pitch.

All Praise to You, My God, This Night 70

May be sung in canon

1 All praise to you, my God, this night, for all the bless-ings
2 For - give me, Lord, for this I pray, the wrong that I have
3 Lord, may I be at rest in you and sweet - ly sleep the
4 Praise God, from whom all bless-ings flow; praise him, all crea-tures

of the light. Keep me, O keep me, King of kings,
done this day. May peace with God and neigh - bor be,
whole night through. Re - fresh my strength, for your own sake,
here be - low. Praise him a - bove, you heav - enly host;

for canon only

be - neath the shel - ter of your wings. (-ter of your wings.)
be - fore I sleep, re - stored to me. (re - stored to me.)
so I may serve you when I wake. (you when I wake.)
praise Fa - ther, Son, and Ho - ly Ghost. (and Ho - ly Ghost.)

Words: Thomas Ken (1709), alt., P.D.
Music: Thomas Tallis (ca. 1561), P.D.

88 88
TALLIS' CANON

Anglican bishop Ken wrote a group of three hymns for morning, evening, and midnight devotions for Winchester College students. This text is the evening hymn, revised by Ken for the 1709 edition of his *A Manual of Prayers.* TALLIS CANON was one of nine tunes Tallis contributed to Matthew Parker's *Psalter* (c. 1561), and has enjoyed a long association with Ken's text.

71 The Strife Is O'er, the Battle Done

Alleluia, alleluia, alleluia!

1 The strife is o'er, the bat - tle done; the vic - to - ry of
2 The powers of death have done their worst, but Christ their le - gions
3 The three sad days are quick - ly sped; he ris - es glo - rious
4 He closed the yawn - ing gates of hell; the bars from heaven's high

life is won; the song of tri - umph has be - gun.
has dis-persed. Let shouts of ho - ly joy out - burst.
from the dead. All glo - ry to our ris - en Head.
por - tals fell. Let hymns of praise his tri - umph tell.

Al - le - lu - ia!

5 Lord, by the stripes which wounded thee,
   from death's dread sting thy servants free,
   that we may live and sing to thee. Alleluia!
   Alleluia, alleluia, alleluia!

Words: *Symphonia Sirenum,* Cologne (1695); tr. Francis Pott (1861), P.D.
Music: Giovanni da Palestrina (1591); adapt. and arr. William H. Monk (1861), P.D.

888 with alleluias
VICTORY

This Easter hymn depicts Christ's resurrection as his great victory over the powers of evil, just as Paul does in 1 Corinthians 15. First published in a Jesuit hymnal, the text is surrounded by Easter "alleluias," which give life to the sober melody of the stanzas. Palestrina's tune comes from one of his many Magnificat settings which Monk prepared for *Hymns Ancient and Modern.*

While Shepherds Watched Their Flocks 72

1 While shep - herds watched their flocks by night, all
2 "Fear not," said he— for might - y dread had
3 "To you, in Dav - id's town, this day is
4 "The heav - enly babe you there shall find to

seat - ed on the ground, an an - gel of the
seized their trou - bled mind— "glad tid - ings of great
born of Dav - id's line a Sav - ior, who is
hu - man view dis - played, all sim - ply wrapped in

Lord came down, and glo - ry shone a - round.
joy I bring to you and all man - kind.
Christ the Lord; and this shall be the sign:
swad - dling clothes and in a man - ger laid."

5 Thus spoke the angel. Suddenly
appeared a shining throng
of angels praising God, who thus
addressed their joyful song:

6 "All glory be to God on high,
and to the earth be peace;
to those on whom his favor rests
goodwill shall never cease."

Words: Luke 2:8-14; vers. Nahum Tate (1700), alt. P.D.
Music: Thomas Este's *The Whole book of Psalms* (1592), P.D.

86 86
WINCHESTER OLD

This Christmas narrative of the shepherds was versified and published by Tate in a supplement to the "New Version Psalter" (1700) by Tate and Nicholas Brady. The psalm-tune commonly associated with this text is attributed to George Kirbye; text and music have been inseparable since their first appearance in *Hymns Ancient and Modern* (1861).

73 Come, We That Love the Lord/ We're Marching to Zion

1 Come, we that love the Lord, and let our joys be known; join
2 Let those re-fuse to sing who nev-er knew our God; but

in a song with sweet ac-cord, join in a song with sweet ac-cord,
chil-dren of the heaven-ly King, but chil-dren of the heaven-ly King

and thus sur-round the throne, and thus sur-round the throne.
may speak their joys a-broad, may speak their joys a-broad.

Refrain

We're march-ing to Zi-on, beau-ti-ful, beau-ti-ful Zi-on;

we're march-ing up-ward to Zi-on, the beau-ti-ful cit-y of God.

Words: Isaac Watts (1707); ref. Robert Lowry (1867), P.D.
Music: Robert Lowry (1867), P.D.

66 88 66 with refrain
MARCHING TO ZION

3 The hill of Zion yields a thousand sacred sweets
before we reach the heavenly fields,
before we reach the heavenly fields
or walk the golden streets,
or walk the golden streets. *Refrain*

4 Then let our songs abound, and every tear be dry;
we're marching through Emmanuel's ground,
we're marching through Emmanuel's ground
to fairer worlds on high,
to fairer worlds on high. *Refrain*

Somewhat like the psalms of ascent in the Old Testament (Psalms 120-134), this text is a pilgrimage song about the Christian journey from this earth to a new heaven and earth. Lowry's tune has been hailed as a "lively quickstep for happy Christians." Lowry intended adults to sing the stanzas, with children joining on the refrain.

74 When I Survey the Wondrous Cross

1 When I sur-vey the won-drous cross on which the
2 For-bid it, Lord, that I should boast save in the
3 See, from his head, his hands, his feet, sor-row and
4 Were the whole realm of na-ture mine, that were a

Prince of glo-ry died, my rich-est gain I
death of Christ, my God! All the vain things that
love flow min-gled down. Did e'er such love and
pres-ent far too small. Love so a-maz-ing,

count but loss, and pour con-tempt on all my pride.
charm me most, I sac-ri-fice them through his blood.
sor-row meet, or thorns com-pose so rich a crown?
so di-vine, de-mands my soul, my life, my all.

Words: Isaac Watts (1707), P.D.
Music: Lowell Mason (1824), P.D.

88 88
HAMBURG

Watts' text is a memorably concise sung sermon on the meaning of Christ's atonement, originally published among a group of hymns for the Lord's Supper in his *Hymns and Spiritual Songs* (1707). Many hymnals offer Mason's meditative chant-derived tune for this text; other hymnals provide ROCKINGHAM as a more dramatic tune for these powerful words.

I Sing the Mighty Power of God 75

1 I sing the might-y power of God that made the moun-tains rise,
2 We sing the good-ness of the Lord that filled the earth with food;
3 There's not a plant or flower be-low but makes your glo-ries known,

that spread the flow-ing seas a-broad and built the loft-y skies.
he formed the crea-tures with his word and then pro-nounced them good.
and clouds a-rise and tem-pests blow by or-der from your throne;

I sing the wis-dom that or-dained the sun to rule the day;
Lord, how your won-ders are dis-played, wher-e'er we turn our eyes,
while all that bor-rows life from you is ev-er in your care,

the moon shines full at his com-mand, and all the stars o-bey.
if we sur-vey the ground we tread or gaze up-on the skies.
and ev-ery-where that we can be, you, God, are pres-ent there.

Words: Isaac Watts (1715), alt., P.D.
Music: English; adapt. and harm. Ralph Vaughan Williams (1906), P.D.

86 86 D
KINGSFOLD

Published in his *Divine and Moral Songs for the Use of Children* (1715), Watts wrote this text to help children
(and adults) praise God "for creation and providence" in vivid picturesque language. KINGSFOLD is a folk tune
set to a variety of texts in England and Ireland; Vaughan Williams introduced it as a hymn tune in the *English
Hymnal* (1906).

76   I Love the Lord, He Heard My Cry

1 I love the Lord; he heard my cry
2 I love the Lord; he heard my cry

and pit - ied ev - ery groan.
and chased my grief a - way.

Long as I live and trou - bles rise,
O let my heart no more des - pair

I'll has - ten to his throne.
while I have breath to pray.

Words: Psalm 116:1-2; vers. Isaac Watts (1719), P.D.   86 86
Music: African-American spiritual; harm. Richard Smallwood (1975) © 1975 Century Oak   SMALLWOOD
    Publishing Group/ Richwood Music (admin. MCS America.)

This text is the opening excerpt from Watts' paraphrase of Psalm 116 from his *The Psalms of David Imitated*. Watts'
psalms and hymns quickly spread from England to North America and were used by the white colonists and also
taught to their black slaves. This setting is an example of the African-American appropriation of Watts' texts.

Jesus Shall Reign   77

1 Je - sus shall reign wher - e'er the sun does its suc -
2 To him shall end - less prayer be made, and prais - es
3 Peo - ple and realms of ev - ery tongue dwell on his
4 Bless - ings a - bound wher - e'er he reigns: the pris-oners

ces - sive jour - neys run, his king - dom stretch from
throng to crown his head. His name like sweet per -
love with sweet - est song, and in - fant voic - es
leap to lose their chains, the wea - ry find e -

shore to shore, till moons shall wax and wane no more.
fume shall rise with ev - ery morn - ing sac - ri - fice.
shall pro - claim their ear - ly bless - ings on his name.
ter - nal rest, and all who suf - fer want are blest.

5 Let every creature rise and bring
   the highest honors to our King,
   angels descend with songs again,
   and earth repeat the loud amen.

Words: Isaac Watts (1719), alt; based on Psalm 72, P.D.   88 88
Music: John Hatton (1793), P.D.   DUKE STREET

Watts titled his Christological paraphrase of this portion of the messianic psalm "Christ's Kingdom among the
Gentiles" and gave his text a strong missionary focus. Hatton is virtually anonymous, but his DUKE STREET is a
sturdy and much-loved melody for this text and for "I Know That My Redeemer Lives!" (108); the harmony comes
mostly from the *English Hymnal* (1906).

78 Joy to the World! the Lord Is Come

1 Joy to the world! the Lord is come: let earth re-ceive her King.
2 Joy to the earth! the Sav-ior reigns: let all their songs em-ploy,

Let ev-ery heart pre-pare him room,
while fields and floods, rocks, hills, and plains

and heaven and na-ture sing, and heaven and na-
re - peat the sound-ing joy, re - peat the sound-
and heaven and na-ture sing,

ture sing, and heav-en, and heaven and na-ture sing.
ing joy, re - peat, re - peat the sound-ing joy.

and heaven and na-ture sing,

3 No more let sin and sorrow grow
 nor thorns infest the ground;
 he comes to make his blessings flow
 far as the curse is found,
 far as the curse is found,
 far as, far as the curse is found.

4 He rules the world with truth and grace,
 and makes the nations prove
 the glories of his righteousness
 and wonders of his love,
 and wonders of his love,
 and wonders, wonders of his love.

Words: Isaac Watts (1719); based on Psalm 98, P.D.
Music: Lowell Mason (1848), P.D.

86 86 with repeats
ANTIOCH

This is Watts' Christological interpretation and loose paraphrase of Psalm 98 (e.g., "far as the curse is found" isn't in the biblical text). Though this psalm is appointed for use at Christmas, the hymn merits singing throughout the year. Mason adapted the fusing of several musical phrases from Handel's *Messiah* for Watts' text from a British tunebook; that *Messiah* heritage has made this a hallowed hymn, notwithstanding criticisms of the text.

O God, Our Help in Ages Past 79

1 O God, our help in a - ges past, our hope for years to come,
2 un - der the shad-ow of your throne your saints have dwelt se - cure;
3 Be - fore the hills in or - der stood or earth re - ceived its frame,
4 A thou-sand a - ges in your sight are like an eve - ning gone,

our shel - ter from the storm - y blast, and our e - ter - nal home:
suf - fi - cient is your arm a - lone, and our de - fense is sure.
from ev - er - last - ing you are God, to end - less years the same.
short as the watch that ends the night be - fore the ris - ing sun.

5 Time, like an ever-rolling stream,
   soon bears us all away;
   we fly forgotten, as a dream
   dies at the opening day.

6 O God, our help in ages past,
   our hope for years to come,
   still be our guard while troubles last,
   and our eternal home!

Words: Psalm 90:1-2, 4-5; vers. Isaac Watts (1719), alt., P.D.
Music: William Croft (1708), P.D.

86 86
ST. ANNE

Extracted from the opening section of Psalm 90, Watts' famous paraphrase expresses great assurance, promise, and hope in the Lord; it functions as a second national anthem in Britain. The long-lasting union of Watts' text and Croft's majestic tune was first fashioned in *Hymns Ancient and Modern* (1861).

80　And Can It Be

1 And can it be that I should gain an in - terest in the
2 He left his Fa - ther's throne a - bove—so free, so in - fi -
3 Long my im - pris - oned spir - it lay fast bound in sin and
4 No con - dem - na - tion now I dread, for Christ, and all in

Sav - ior's blood? Died he for me, who caused his pain— for
nite his grace— emp - tied him - self of all but love, and
na - ture's night. Your sun - rise turned that night to day; I
him, is mine! A - live in him, my liv - ing Head, and

me, who caused his bit - ter death? A - maz - ing love! How
bled for Ad - am's help - less race! What mer - cy this, im -
woke— the dun - geon flamed with light! My chains fell off, your
clothed in right - eous - ness di - vine, bold I ap - proach the e -

can it be that you, my Lord, should die for me?
mense and free, for, O my God, it found out me!
voice I knew; I rose, went out, and fol - lowed you.
ter - nal throne and claim the crown, through Christ, my own.

Words: Charles Wesley (1738), alt., P.D.
Music: Thomas Campbell (1825), P.D.

88 88 88 with refrain
SAGINA

Refrain

A - maz - ing love! How can it be that
A - maz - ing love! How can it be

you, my Lord, should die for me?
that you, my Lord,

Charles Wesley wrote this text shortly after his conversion in London and sang it with his brother, John, after John's similar "Aldersgate experience." Subtitled "Free Grace," it is one of the great hymns of Methodism that has received wide ecumenical acceptance. SAGINA is a melismatic tune (one that often uses several notes per syllable) which is a late survivor beyond the time of the Wesleys when such tunes were popular.

81 Christ the Lord Is Risen Today

May be sung antiphonally

1 Christ the Lord is risen to-day! Al - le-lu - ia!
2 Love's re-deem-ing work is done, Al - le-lu - ia!
3 Lives a-gain our glo-rious King; Al - le-lu - ia!

All cre-a-tion, join to say: Al - le-lu - ia!
Fought the fight, the bat-tle won; Al - le-lu - ia!
Where, O death, is now your sting? Al - le-lu - ia!

Raise your joys and tri-umphs high; Al - le-lu - ia!
Death in vain for-bids him rise; Al - le-lu - ia!
Once he died, our souls to save; Al - le-lu - ia!

Sing, O heavens, and earth, re-ply: Al - le-lu - ia!
Christ has o-pened par-a-dise. Al - le-lu - ia!
Where your vic-to-ry, O grave? Al - le-lu - ia!

Words: Charles Wesley (1739), alt., P.D.
Music: *Lyra Davidica* (1708), P.D.

77 77 with alleluias
EASTER HYMN

4 Soar we now where Christ has led, Alleluia!
Following our exalted Head; Alleluia!
Made like him, like him we rise; Alleluia!
Ours the cross, the grave, the skies. Alleluia!

5 Hail the Lord of earth and heaven! Alleluia!
Praise to you by both be given; Alleluia!
Risen Christ, triumphant now; Alleluia!
Every knee to you shall bow. Alleluia!

Wesley's "Hymn for Easter Day" expresses the great themes of Easter, surrounded by multiple "alleluias" that were added by later editors to suit this joyous tune. This hymn invites antiphonal performance in the text phrases and the "alleluias."

82 Hark! the Herald Angels Sing

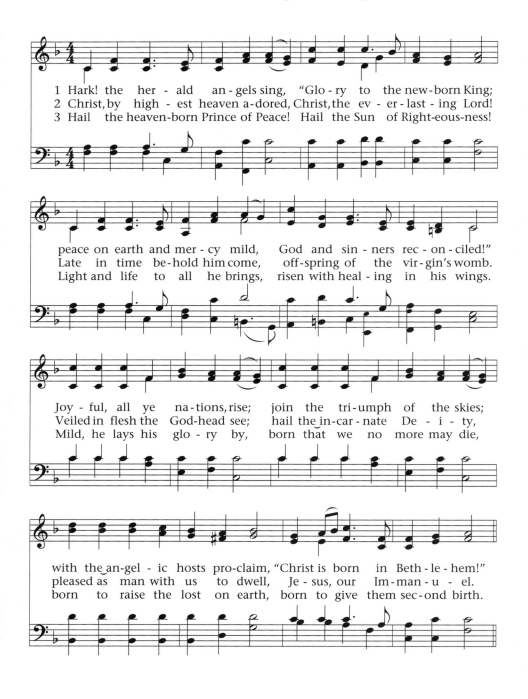

1 Hark! the her-ald an-gels sing, "Glo-ry to the new-born King;
2 Christ, by high-est heaven a-dored, Christ, the ev-er-last-ing Lord!
3 Hail the heaven-born Prince of Peace! Hail the Sun of Right-eous-ness!

peace on earth and mer-cy mild, God and sin-ners rec-on-ciled!"
Late in time be-hold him come, off-spring of the vir-gin's womb.
Light and life to all he brings, risen with heal-ing in his wings.

Joy-ful, all ye na-tions, rise; join the tri-umph of the skies;
Veiled in flesh the God-head see; hail the in-car-nate De-i-ty,
Mild, he lays his glo-ry by, born that we no more may die,

with the an-gel-ic hosts pro-claim, "Christ is born in Beth-le-hem!"
pleased as man with us to dwell, Je-sus, our Im-man-u-el.
born to raise the lost on earth, born to give them sec-ond birth.

Words: Charles Wesley (1739), alt., P.D.
Music: Felix Mendelssohn (1840); adapt. William H. Cummings (1856), P.D.

77 77 D with refrain
MENDELSSOHN

Hark! the her-ald an-gels sing, "Glo-ry to the new-born King!"

Wesley originally began this "Hymn for Christmas Day" with the following: "Hark, how all the welkin [heavens] rings glory to the King of kings." It is one of our finest Christmas hymns because of its mix of exclamation, exhortation, and theological reflection on Christ's incarnation. Though Mendelssohn never intended this rousing melody from his *Festgesang*, Op. 68 to be used in church, the union of Wesley's text and Mendelssohn's tune in *Hymns Ancient and Modern* (1861) has remained popular.

83 Jesus, Lover of My Soul

1 Je - sus, lov - er of my soul, let me to thy bo - som fly,
2 Oth - er ref - uge have I none; hangs my help-less soul on thee;
3 Plen-teous grace with thee is found, grace to cov - er all my sin;

while the near - er wa - ters roll, while the tem-pest still is high;
leave, ah! leave me not a - lone, still sup - port and com-fort me.
let the heal - ing streams a-bound; make and keep me pure with - in.

hide me, O my Sav - ior, hide, till the storm of life is past;
All my trust on thee is stayed, all my help from thee I bring;
Thou of life the foun-tain art; free - ly let me take of thee;

safe in - to the ha - ven guide, O re - ceive my soul at last!
cov - er my de-fense-less head with the shad-ow of thy wing.
spring thou up with - in my heart, rise to all e - ter - ni - ty.

Words: Charles Wesley (1738), P.D.
Music: Joseph Parry (1876), P.D.

77 77 D
ABERYSTWYTH

Originally titled "In Temptation," Wesley's text develops the imagery of a person who finds refuge in Christ amid temptation. Parry wrote this music at first for a Welsh text, but then he united it with Wesley's words, surprisingly, in his druid-themed cantata *Ceridwen*. The climax in the melody's penultimate line is one of the glories of sung hymnody.

Oh, for a Thousand Tongues to Sing 84

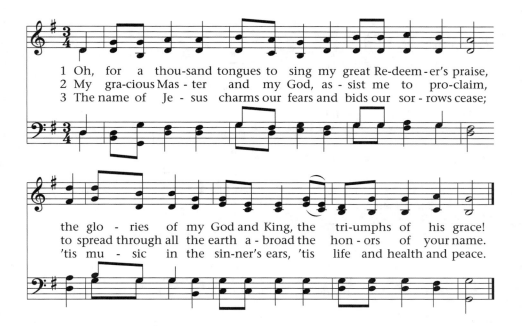

1 Oh, for a thou-sand tongues to sing my great Re-deem-er's praise,
2 My gra-cious Mas - ter and my God, as - sist me to pro-claim,
3 The name of Je - sus charms our fears and bids our sor - rows cease;

the glo - ries of my God and King, the tri-umphs of his grace!
to spread through all the earth a - broad the hon - ors of your name.
'tis mu - sic in the sin-ner's ears, 'tis life and health and peace.

4 He breaks the power of canceled sin,
he sets the prisoner free;
his blood can make the foulest clean;
his blood avails for me.

5 He speaks, and, listening to his voice,
new life the dead receive;
the mournful, broken hearts rejoice;
the humble poor believe.

6 Hear him, you deaf; you voiceless ones,
your loosened tongues employ;
you blind, behold your Savior come;
and leap, you lame, for joy!

7 To God all glory, praise, and love
be now and ever given
by saints below and saints above,
the church in earth and heaven.

Words: Charles Wesley (1739), alt., P.D.
Music: Carl G. Gläser (1828); adapt. and arr. Lowell Mason (1839), P.D.

86 86
AZMON

Beginning "Glory to God, and praise and love," Wesley wrote an eighteen-stanza hymn in 1739 to celebrate his conversion a year earlier. "Oh, for a Thousand Tongues" consists of select stanzas from this longer text, and is often the first hymn in Methodist hymnals. Gläser's melody appeared in duple rhythm in Mason's *Modern Psalmist* (1839), but in later publications he changed it to triple meter.

85 Come, Thou Long-Expected Jesus

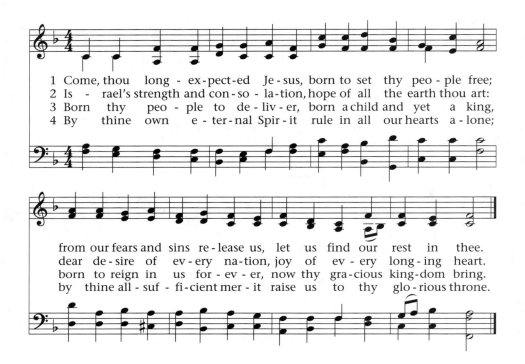

1 Come, thou long-ex-pect-ed Je-sus, born to set thy peo-ple free;
2 Is - rael's strength and con-so-la-tion, hope of all the earth thou art:
3 Born thy peo-ple to de-liv-er, born a child and yet a king,
4 By thine own e-ter-nal Spir-it rule in all our hearts a-lone;

from our fears and sins re-lease us, let us find our rest in thee.
dear de-sire of ev-ery na-tion, joy of ev-ery long-ing heart.
born to reign in us for-ev-er, now thy gra-cious king-dom bring.
by thine all-suf-fi-cient mer-it raise us to thy glo-rious throne.

Words: Charles Wesley (1744), P.D.   87 87
Music: Christian F. Witt's *Psalmodia Sacra* (1715); adapt. Henry J. Gauntlett (1861), P.D.   STUTTGART

Wesley's compact Advent hymn helps us remember Christ's first coming even while praying for his second coming and his rule in our lives. Gauntlett changed the rhythmic setting of Witt's tune into isorhythm (all equal rhythms) for use in *Hymns Ancient and Modern* (1861).

Rejoice, the Lord Is King 86

1 Re - joice, the Lord is King! Your Lord and King a - dore.
2 His king - dom can - not fail; he rules o'er earth and heaven;
3 He sits at God's right hand till all his foes sub - mit,
4 Re - joice in glo - rious hope; for Christ, the Judge, shall come

Re - joice, give thanks and sing and tri - umph ev - er - more.
the keys of death and hell to Christ the Lord are given.
bow down at his com - mand, and fall be - neath his feet.
to gath - er all his saints to their e - ter - nal home.

Lift up your heart, lift up your voice.
Lift up your heart, lift up your voice.
Lift up your heart, lift up your voice.
We soon shall hear the arch - an - gel's voice;

Re - joice, a - gain I say, re - joice!
Re - joice, a - gain I say, re - joice!
Re - joice, a - gain I say, re - joice!
the trump of God shall sound, re - joice!

Words: Charles Wesley (1744), alt., P.D.
Music: John Darwall (1770), P.D.

66 66 88
DARWALL'S 148

Written for use at Easter and Ascension, Wesley's text exalts Christ as king and features Paul's injunction to "rejoice" as its keynote. An Anglican preacher and amateur musician, Darwall first composed this tune for Psalm 148; it is the only one of his 150 psalm melodies in common use today.

87 You Servants of God, Your Master Proclaim

1 You ser-vants of God, your Mas-ter pro-claim,
2 God rules in the height, al-might-y to save;
3 "Sal-va-tion to God, who sits on the throne!"
4 Then let us a-dore and give him his right:

and pub-lish a-broad his won-der-ful name;
though hid from our sight, his pres-ence we have;
let all cry a-loud, and hon-or the Son;
all glo-ry and power, all wis-dom and might,

the name all-vic-to-rious of Je-sus ex-tol;
the great con-gre-ga-tion his tri-umph shall sing,
the prais-es of Je-sus the an-gels pro-claim,
all hon-or and bless-ing— with an-gels a-bove—

his king-dom is glo-rious and rules o-ver all.
as-crib-ing sal-va-tion to Je-sus, our King.
fall down on their fac-es and wor-ship the Lamb.
and thanks nev-er ceas-ing for in-fi-nite love.

Words: Charles Wesley (19744), alt., P.D.
Music: attr. William Croft (1708), P.D.

10 10 11 11
HANOVER

These stanzas are selected from a larger text in which Wesley wanted to reassure and comfort the early Methodist societies in their frequent "times of trouble and persecution." Initially ascribed to Handel, Croft's music is one of several tunes associated with this text, and comes from a supplement to the "New Version Psalter."

Love Divine, All Loves Excelling 88

1 Love di-vine, all loves ex-cel-ling, Joy of heaven, to earth come down;
2 Come, Al-might-y, to de-liv-er, let us all thy life re-ceive;
3 Fin-ish, then, thy new cre-a-tion; pure and spot-less let us be;

fix in us thy hum-ble dwell-ing, all thy faith-ful mer-cies crown.
sud-den-ly re-turn, and nev-er, nev-er-more thy tem-ples leave.
let us see thy great sal-va-tion per-fect-ly re-stored in thee;

Je - sus, thou art all com-pas-sion, pure, un-bound-ed love thou art;
Thee we would be al-ways bless-ing, serve thee with thy hosts a-bove,
changed from glo-ry in-to glo-ry, till in heaven we take our place,

vis-it us with thy sal-va-tion, en-ter ev-ery trem-bling heart.
pray and praise thee with-out ceas-ing, glo-ry in thy per-fect love.
till we cast our crowns be-fore thee, lost in won-der, love, and praise.

Words: Charles Wesley (1747), P.D.
Music: Rowland H. Prichard (1831), P.D.

87 87 D
HYFRYDOL

Thought to be among the finest of the Wesley texts, "Love Divine" is a prayer hymn for the indwelling of Christ in our lives that leads to a profession of the Wesleyan doctrine of perfection in stanza 3. Singing these words to the great Welsh melody HYFRYDOL is one of the abiding unions of text and tune in all of hymnody. This tune with a different harmonization is used with "I Will Sing of My Redeemer" (191).

89 Lo! He Comes with Clouds Descending

1 Lo! he comes, with clouds de-scend-ing, once for our sal-
2 Ev-ery eye shall now be-hold him, robed in dread-ful
3 Those dear to-kens of his pas-sion still his daz-zling

va-tion slain; thou-sand thou-sand saints at-tend-ing swell
maj-es-ty; those who set at naught and sold him, pierced,
bo-dy bears, cause of end-less ex-ul-ta-tion to

the tri-umph of his train: Al-le-lu-ia! Al-le-
and nailed him to the tree, deep-ly wail-ing, deep-ly
his ran-somed wor-ship-ers; with what rap-ture, with what

lu-ia! Al-le-lu-ia! Christ the Lord re-turns to reign.
wail-ing, deep-ly wail-ing, shall the true Mes-si-ah see.
rap-ture, with what rap-ture gaze we on those glo-rious scars!

4 Yea, amen! let all adore thee, high on thine eternal throne;
  Savior, take the power and glory, claim the kingdom for thine own:
  Alleluia! Alleluia! Alleluia! Thou shalt reign, and thou alone.

Words: Charles Wesley (1758), P.D.
Music: 18th c. English melody; attr. Thomas Olivers (1765); harm. Ralph Vaughan
   Williams (1906), P.D.

87 87 47
HELMSLEY

This hymn resulted when Wesley totally rewrote the text of an Advent hymn by his friend John Cennick. The melismas (i.e., several musical notes per syllable of text) of this setting given here were a common feature of hymn tunes in the Wesley songbooks, but HELMSLEY is one of the few that survives in more recent hymnals, as syllabic settings (one note per syllable of text) appear to be normative for congregational singing.

O For a Closer Walk with God   90

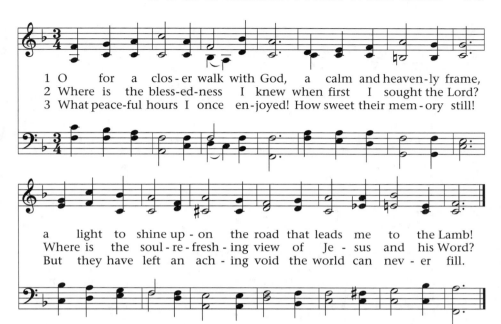

1 O for a clos-er walk with God, a calm and heaven-ly frame,
2 Where is the bless-ed-ness I knew when first I sought the Lord?
3 What peace-ful hours I once en-joyed! How sweet their mem-ory still!

a light to shine up-on the road that leads me to the Lamb!
Where is the soul-re-fresh-ing view of Je - sus and his Word?
But they have left an ach-ing void the world can nev-er fill.

4 The dearest idol I have known,
   whate'er that idol be,
   help me to tear it from thy throne
   and worship only thee.

5 So shall my walk be close with God,
   calm and serene my frame;
   so purer light shall mark the road
   that leads me to the Lamb.

Words: William Cowper (1772), P.D.
Music: John B. Dykes (1875), P.D.

86 86
BEATITUDO

Cowper, who battled depression all his life, wrote this text to "surrender to God" his concerns about the illness of his host and housekeeper, Mrs. Unwin. It was revised for the *Olney Hymns* (1779), the collection of hymns by Cowper and John Newton. Dykes' tune was composed for the 1875 edition of *Hymns Ancient and Modern*.

91 There Is a Fountain Filled with Blood

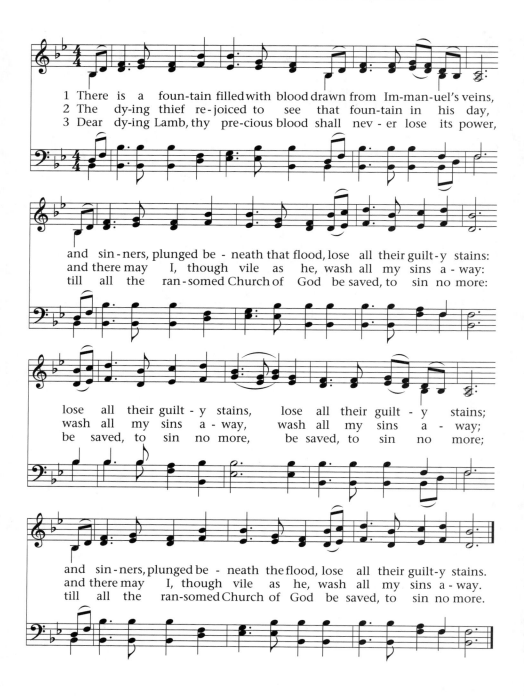

1 There is a foun-tain filled with blood drawn from Im-man-uel's veins,
2 The dy-ing thief re-joiced to see that foun-tain in his day,
3 Dear dy-ing Lamb, thy pre-cious blood shall nev - er lose its power,

and sin-ners, plunged be - neath that flood, lose all their guilt-y stains:
and there may I, though vile as he, wash all my sins a - way:
till all the ran-somed Church of God be saved, to sin no more:

lose all their guilt - y stains, lose all their guilt - y stains;
wash all my sins a - way, wash all my sins a - way;
be saved, to sin no more, be saved, to sin no more;

and sin-ners, plunged be - neath the flood, lose all their guilt-y stains.
and there may I, though vile as he, wash all my sins a - way.
till all the ran-somed Church of God be saved, to sin no more.

Words: William Cowper (1771), P.D.
Music: Traditional American melody; arr. Lowell Mason (1830), P.D.

86 86 66 86
CLEANSING FOUNTAIN

4 E'er since by faith I saw the stream
   thy flowing wounds supply,
   redeeming love has been my theme,
   and shall be till I die:
   and shall be till I die,
   and shall be till I die;
   redeeming love has been my theme,
   and shall be till I die.

5 When this poor lisping, stammering tongue
   lies silent in the grave,
   then in a nobler, sweeter song
   I'll sing thy power to save:
   I'll sing thy power to save,
   I'll sing thy power to save;
   then in a nobler, sweeter song
   I'll sing thy power to save.

Cowper's words draw on Zechariah 13:1, the gospel narrative of the penitent thief on the cross next to Jesus, and "blood" theology (on which scholars hold mixed opinions)—all leading to a personal confession of Christ's saving power. The tune comes from the camp meeting tradition.

92 God Moves in a Mysterious Way

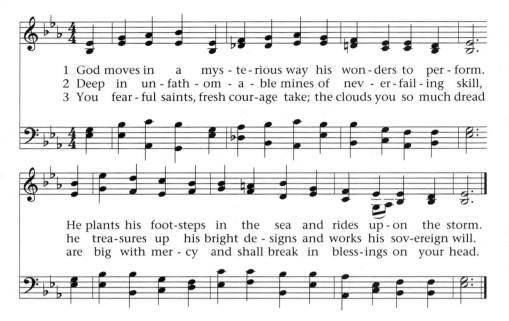

1 God moves in a mys-te-rious way his won-ders to per-form.
2 Deep in un-fath-om-a-ble mines of nev-er-fail-ing skill,
3 You fear-ful saints, fresh cour-age take; the clouds you so much dread

He plants his foot-steps in the sea and rides up-on the storm.
he trea-sures up his bright de-signs and works his sov-ereign will.
are big with mer-cy and shall break in bless-ings on your head.

4 His purposes will ripen fast,
   unfolding every hour.
   The bud may have a bitter taste,
   but sweet will be the flower.

5 Blind unbelief is sure to err
   and scan his work in vain.
   God is his own interpreter,
   and he will make it plain.

Words: William Cowper (1774), P.D.   86 86
Music: Scottish Psalter (1615); harm. Thomas Ravenscroft (1621), alt., P.D.   DUNDEE

The fine English poet Cowper suffered from severe depressions and wrote this text at the beginning of one of those difficult periods in his life. When published in the *Olney Hymns* (1779), produced jointly by Cowper and John Newton, it received the fitting heading "Light Shining Out of Darkness." The dreary equal-notes or isorhythmic version of DUNDEE (also known as FRENCH) is fortunately graced with a few interesting harmonies.

How Sweet the Name of Jesus Sounds 93

1 How sweet the name of Je - sus sounds in
2 It makes the wound - ed spir - it whole and
3 O Je - sus, Shep - herd, Guard - ian, Friend, my

a be - liev - er's ear! It soothes our sor - rows,
calms the trou - bled breast; 'tis man - na to the
Proph - et, Priest, and King, my Lord, my Life, my

heals our wounds, and drives a - way our fear.
hun - gry soul, and to the wea - ry, rest.
Way, my End, ac - cept the praise I bring.

4 How weak the effort of my heart,
   how cold my warmest thought;
   but when I see you as you are,
   I'll praise you as I ought.

5 Till then I would your love proclaim
   with every fleeting breath;
   and may the music of your name
   refresh my soul in death.

Words: John Newton (1779), P.D.
Music: Alexander R. Reinagle (1836), P.D.

86 86
ST. PETER

This text is an *Olney Hymns* example of Newton's evangelical piety and his skill in incorporating biblical phrases and allusions in his hymns, including in this instance various names and images of Christ. Reinagle's tune was first set to Newton's text in *Hymns Ancient and Modern* (1861); that union of text and tune has survived in most modern hymnals.

94 Amazing Grace—How Sweet the Sound

1 A - maz - ing grace— how sweet the sound— that saved a wretch like me! I once was lost, but now am found, was blind, but now I see.

2 'Twas grace that taught my heart to fear, and grace my fears re-lieved; how pre - cious did that grace ap - pear the hour I first be - lieved!

3 The Lord has prom - ised good to me, his word my hope se - cures; he will my shield and por - tion be as long as life en - dures.

4 Through many dangers, toils, and snares
I have already come;
'tis grace hath brought me safe thus far,
and grace will lead me home.

5 When we've been there ten thousand years,
bright shining as the sun,
we've no less days to sing God's praise
than when we'd first begun.

Words: st. 1-4, John Newton (1779); st. 5, *A Collection of Sacred Ballads* (1790), P.D.
Music: *Virginia Harmony* (1831); adapt. and harm. Edwin O. Excell (1900), P.D.

86 86
NEW BRITAIN

One of the most-loved English hymns, "Amazing Grace" is an autobiographical text by Newton that stresses the belief that we are saved by grace alone. One of the many popular settings of this pentatonic tune is by Excell—a songleader, gospel hymn composer, and publisher. The other version here demonstrates its shape-note setting in the *Columbian Harmony*, but it originally featured another text. Newton's text and NEW BRITAIN were united for

1 A - maz - ing grace— how sweet the sound— that

saved a wretch like me! I once was lost, but

now am found, was blind, but now I see.

the first time in William Walker's *Southern Harmony* (1835). Shape-note notation developed initially as a mnemonic aid and contributed to important songbooks such as *Southern Harmony* and Benjamin White and Elisha King's *The Sacred Harp* (1844)—both of which are still used in modern shape-note singing. In such singing, men and women typically mix on some or all of the parts and thus create more than four-part harmony. The melody line is traditionally in the tenor part. It is customary to sing the music in fa-sol-la syllables before singing the actual text of the hymn.

95 Glorious Things Of You Are Spoken

1 Glo - rious things of you are spo - ken, Zi - on, cit - y
2 See, the streams of liv - ing wa - ters, spring - ing from e -
3 Round each hab - i - ta - tion hov - ering, see the cloud and
4 Sav - ior, since of Zi - on's cit - y I through grace a

of our God. He whose word can - not be bro - ken formed you
ter - nal love, well sup - ply your sons and daugh - ters and all
fire ap - pear for a glo - ry and a cover - ing, show - ing
mem - ber am, let the world de - ride or pit - y, I will

for his own a - bode. On the Rock of A - ges found - ed,
fear of want re - move. Who can faint while such a riv - er
that the Lord is near. Thus de - riv - ing from their ban - ner
glo - ry in your name. Fad - ing are the world's best plea - sures,

what can shake your sure re - pose? With sal - va - tion's
ev - er will their thirst as - suage? Grace, which like the
light by night and shade by day, safe they feed up -
all its boast - ed pomp and show; sol - id joys and

Words: John Newton (1779), alt., P.D.
Music: Franz J. Haydn (1796), P.D.

87 87 D
AUSTRIA

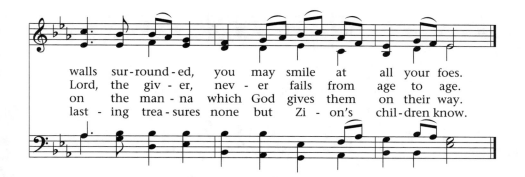

walls sur-round-ed, you may smile at all your foes.
Lord, the giv-er, nev-er fails from age to age.
on the man-na which God gives them on their way.
last-ing trea-sures none but Zi-on's chil-dren know.

Inspired by Isaiah 33:20-21 and the Old Testament psalms that focus on Zion as the city of God, Newton also included many New Testament allusions in this text, which he published in the *Olney Hymns*. Haydn initially wrote
the tune to be used as the Austrian national anthem, and the Nazis used it for their anthem, but it migrated into
various hymnals early in its history and has remained a worthy hymn tune today.

96 Christian Hearts in Love United

1 Chris - tian hearts in love u - nit - ed: search to know God's ho - ly will.
2 Grant, Lord, that with your di - rec-tion, "Love each oth - er" we com-ply.
3 Come, then, liv - ing church of Je - sus, cov - e - nant with him a - new.

Let his love, in us ig - nit - ed, more and more our spir-its fill.
Help us live in true af - fec - tion, your love to ex - em pli - fy.
Un - to him who con - quered for us may we pledge our ser-vice true.

Christ the head, and we his mem-bers— we re - flect the light he is.
Let our mu - tual love be glow - ing bright-ly so that all may view
May our lives re - flect the bright-ness of God's love in Je - sus shown.

Christ the mas - ter, we dis - ci - ples—he is ours and we are his.
that we, as on one stem grow-ing, liv - ing branch-es are in you.
To the world we then bear wit - ness: we be - long to God a - lone.

Words: Nicolaus L. von Zinzendorf (1723); tr. composite, P.D.
Music: Moravian chorale book manuscript, Herrnhut (1735), P.D.

87 87 D
O DU LIEBE MEINER LIEBE

These stanzas, which originate in a very long poem on Jesus' teachings in John 14-17, come to us from Zinzendorf, the leader of an outstanding Moravian community of daily piety, worship, and missionary zeal in Herrnhut during the eighteenth century. The tune had Roman Catholic roots before its use by the Moravians.

Jesus, Still Lead On 97

1 Je - sus, still lead on, till our rest be won; and, al -
2 If the way be drear, if the foe be near, let no
3 When we seek re - lief from a long - felt grief; when temp -
4 Je - sus, still lead on, till our rest be won; heaven - ly

though the way be cheer - less, we will fol - low, calm and
faith - less fears o'er - take us, let not faith and hope for -
ta - tions come al - lur - ing, make us pa - tient and en -
lead - er, still di - rect us, still sup - port, con - sole, pro -

fear - less. Guide us by your hand to the pro - mised land.
sake us; safe - ly past the foe to our home we go.
dur - ing; show us that bright shore where we weep no more.
tect us, till we safe - ly stand in the pro - mised land.

Words: Nicolaus L. von Zinzendorf (1700-1761); tr. Jane L. Borthwick (1858), alt., P.D.   55 88 55
Music: Adam Drese (1698), P.D.   SEELENBRÄUTIGAM

Stanzas from two of the great Moravian bishop Zinzendorf's many hymn texts were combined by Christian
Gregor in his *Bruder Gesangbuch* (1778) to produce this composite prayer for Christ to lead us on our pilgrim
journey. Drese's melody was first composed for one of his own hymns, but is now firmly wedded to this
Zinzendorf text.

98   God Himself Is with Us

1 God him-self is with us; let us now a-dore him, and with awe appear be-fore him. God is in his tem-ple; all with-in keep si-lence,
pros-trate lie with deep-est rev - erence. Him a-lone do we own
as our God and Sav - ior; praise his name for - ev - er.

2 God himself is with us;
hear the harps resounding!
See the crowds the throne surrounding!
"Holy, holy, holy,"
hear the hymn ascending,
angels, saints, their voices blending!
Bow your ear to us here;
hear, O Christ, the praises
that your church now raises.

3 Fount of every blessing,
purify my spirit,
trusting only in your merit.
Like the holy angels
who behold your glory,
may I ceaselessly adore you,
and in all, great and small,
seek to do most nearly
what you love so dearly.

Words: Gerhardt Tersteegen (1729); tr. composite, P.D.
Music: Joachim Neander (1680), P.D.

668 668 666
ARNSBERG

An important German Reformed mystic, Tersteegen wrote this text after his conversion experience in 1724,
intending it to be sung to this tune by the Pietism-influenced Neander.

Hark, the Glad Sound! The Savior Comes   99

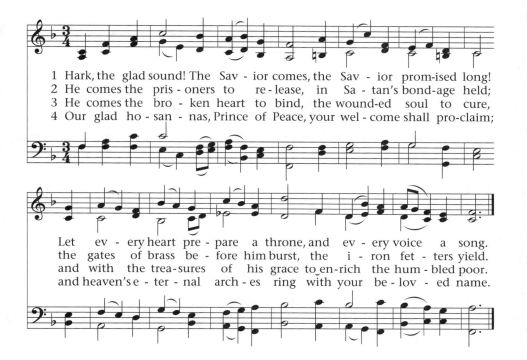

1 Hark, the glad sound! The Sav - ior comes, the Sav - ior prom-ised long!
2 He comes the pris - oners to   re - lease, in   Sa - tan's bond-age held;
3 He comes the bro - ken heart to bind, the wound-ed   soul   to   cure,
4 Our glad ho - san - nas, Prince of Peace, your wel - come shall pro-claim;

Let   ev - ery heart pre - pare   a throne, and   ev - ery voice   a   song.
the   gates   of brass be - fore him burst, the   i - ron fet - ters yield.
and with   the trea-sures   of   his grace to en-rich   the hum - bled poor.
and heaven's e - ter - nal   arch - es   ring   with your   be - lov - ed   name.

Words: Philip Doddridge (1735); based on Isaiah 61:1-2, P.D.   86 86
Music: Thomas Haweis (1792); adapt. Samuel Webbe (1808), P.D.   RICHMOND

This fine Christological text draws on Jesus' use of the Isaiah text in Luke 4, demonstrating the reality of his coming in our daily lives. It was included among the Scottish *Translations and Paraphrases* (1745/1781), and, united with
a revision of Haweis' originally florid melody, it has become a loved Advent hymn.

100 O Come, All Ye Faithful

Words: attr. John F. Wade (1743); tr. Frederick Oakeley (1841), and others, P.D.
Music: attr. John F. Wade (1743), P.D.

irregular
ADESTE FIDELIS

O come, let us a - dore him, Christ the Lord!

Inspired by the Nicene Creed's confession about the incarnation of Christ, Wade's text is one of our finest Christmas hymns, happily devoid of the folksy sentimentality that too often surrounds Jesus' birth. Note two unusual features about these words: they're unrhymed and cast in irregular meter. A Roman Catholic, Wade wrote the text in Latin and the fuguing tune (note the melodic imitation in its refrain) originally in triple meter.

101 Guide Me, O My Great Redeemer

1 Guide me, O my great Re-deem-er, pil-grim through this
2 O-pen now the crys-tal foun-tain, where the heal-ing
3 When I tread the verge of Jor-dan, bid my anx-ious

bar-ren land; I am weak, but you are might-y; hold me with your
wa-ters flow. Let the fire and cloud-y pil-lar lead me all my
fears sub-side. Death of death, and hell's De-struc-tion, land me safe on

pow-er-ful hand. Bread of heav-en, bread of heav-en, feed me
jour-ney through. Strong De-liv-erer, strong De-liv-erer, ev-er
Ca-naan's side. Songs of prais-es, songs of prais-es I will

now and ev-er-more, feed me now and ev-er-more.
be my strength and shield, ev-er be my strength and shield.
ev-er sing to you, I will ev-er sing to you.

Words: William Williams (1745); st. 1 tr. Peter Williams (1771), alt.; st. 2-3 tr. William Williams
(1772), alt., P.D.
Music: John Hughes (1907), P.D.

87 87 877

CWM RHONDDA

The circuit-riding preacher-poet William Williams wrote the original text in Welsh as a "prayer for strength to
go through the wilderness of the world." The opening English line included the term "Jehovah" (an artificial
late-medieval title for God of which many modern Bible translations and hymnal editors no longer approve). The
sturdy, lively tune is a standard at Welsh song festivals, at rugby games, and, happily, in many modern hymnals.
For a different musical setting see #211.

Come, Thou Almighty King 102

1 Come, thou al-might-y King, help us thy
2 Come, thou in-car-nate Word, gird on thy
3 Come, ho-ly Com-fort-er, thy sa-cred
4 To thee, great One in Three, e-ter-nal

name to sing; help us to praise. Fa-ther all-
might-y sword; scat-ter thy foes. Let thine al-
wit-ness bear in this glad hour. Thou who al-
prais-es be hence ev-er-more! Thy sov-ereign

glo-ri-ous, o'er all vic-to-ri-ous,
might-y aid our sure de-fense be made,
might-y art, rule now in ev-ery heart,
maj-es-ty may we in glo-ry see,

come and reign o-ver us, An-cient of Days.
our souls on thee be stayed; thy won-ders show.
and ne'er from us de-part, Spir-it of power.
and to e-ter-ni-ty love and a-dore.

Words: anonymous (1757), alt. P.D.
Music: Felice de Giardini (1769), P.D.

664 6664
ITALIAN HYMN

Filled with names for members of the Godhead, this song has a classic trinitarian structure, ending with a
doxology. The tune is named for Giardini's homeland, though he lived in London for some forty years as a
violinist and composer.

103 Be Still, My Soul

1 Be still, my soul: the Lord is on your side!
2 Be still, my soul: your God will un - der - take
3 Be still, my soul: the hour is has - tening on

Bear pa - tient - ly the cross of grief or pain;
to guide the fu - ture, as he has the past;
when we shall be for - ev - er with the Lord,

leave to your God to or - der and pro - vide—
your hope, your con - fi - dence let noth - ing shake—
when dis - ap - point - ment, grief and fear are gone,

in ev - ery change, he faith - ful will re - main.
all now mys - te - rious shall be bright at last.
sor - row for - got, love's pur - est joys re - stored.

Words: Katherina von Schlegel (1752); tr. Jane L. Borthwick (1855), alt., P.D.
Music: Jean Sibelius (1899); arr. *Hymnal* (1933) © 1933, renewed 1961 Presbyterian
Board of Education (admin. by Westminster John Knox Press)

10 10 10 10 10 10
FINLANDIA

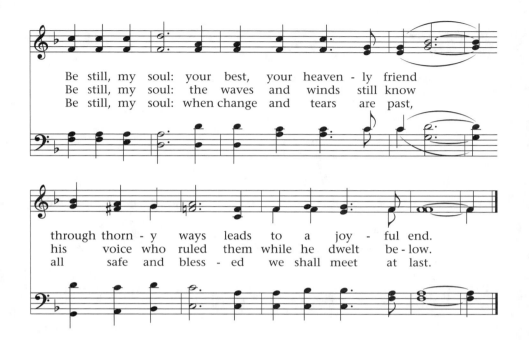

Be still, my soul: your best, your heaven - ly friend
Be still, my soul: the waves and winds still know
Be still, my soul: when change and tears are past,

through thorn - y ways leads to a joy - ful end.
his voice who ruled them while he dwelt be - low.
all safe and bless - ed we shall meet at last.

Shortened from its original six stanzas, this text prevails on us to trust God amidst grief, bereavement, and pain. The tender chorale melody in Sibelius' tone poem *Finlandia*, Opus 26, was first used with this text in the *Church Hymnary* (1927).

104 Come, Thou Fount of Every Blessing

1 Come, thou Fount of ev-ery bless-ing, tune my heart to sing thy grace;

streams of mer-cy, nev-er ceas-ing, call for songs of loud-est praise.

Teach me some me-lo-dious son-net, sung by flam-ing tongues a-bove.

Praise the mount— I'm fixed up-on it—mount of God's re-deem-ing love.

2 Here I find my greatest treasure;
hither by thy help I've come;
and I hope, by thy good pleasure,
safely to arrive at home.
Jesus sought me when a stranger,
wandering from the fold of God;
he, to rescue me from danger,
bought me with his precious blood.

3 Oh, to grace how great a debtor
daily I'm constrained to be!
Let thy goodness, like a fetter,
bind my wandering heart to thee:
prone to wander, Lord, I feel it,
prone to leave the God I love;
here's my heart, O take and seal it;
seal it for thy courts above.

Words: Robert Robinson (1758), alt., P.D.
Music: John Wyeth's *Repository of Sacred Music, Part II* (1813), P.D.

87 87 D
NETTLETON

This text about divine grace and providence contains various biblical images. "Prone to wander" (st. 3) fits Robinson, who became successively a Calvinist Methodist, a Congregationalist, a Baptist, and finally a Unitarian. Wyeth's *Repository* contained shape-note songs for Methodist and Baptist camp meetings.

Come, You Sinners, Poor and Needy   105

1 Come, you sin - ners, poor and need - y, weak and
2 Let not con - science make you lin - ger, nor of
3 Come, you wea - ry, heav - y lad - en, lost and
4 Come, a - rise, and go to Je - sus, he will

wound - ed, sick and sore; Je - sus read - y
fit - ness fond - ly dream; all that he re -
ru - ined by the fall; if you tar - ry
take you in his arms; in the love of

stands to save you, full of pit - y, love, and power.
quires as fit - ness is to know your need of him.
till you're bet - ter, you will nev - er come at all.
your dear Sav - ior you are safe from all a - larms.

Words: Joseph Hart (1759), alt., P.D.
Music: William Walker's *Southern Harmony* (1835), P.D.

87 87
ARISE

Sinners are invited to "arise and go to Jesus" against a backdrop of allusions to Christ's parable of the prodigal son. This pentatonic Appalachian folk melody could be sung as a round, at one measure for each successive entry, to depict various people following each other to Jesus.

106 Lord, Dismiss Us with Your Blessing

1 Lord, dis-miss us with your bless-ing; fill our hearts with
2 Thanks we give and ad - o - ra - tion for your gos-pel's

joy and peace. Let us each, your love pos - sess - ing,
joy - ful sound. May the fruits of your sal - va - tion

tri - umph in re - deem-ing grace. O di - rect us
in our hearts and lives a - bound. Ev - er faith - ful,

and pro - tect us trav - eling through this wil - der - ness.
ev - er faith - ful to your truth may we be found.

Words: attr. John Fawcett (1773), alt., P.D.
Music: Sicilian melody (18th c.), P.D.

87 87 87
SICILIAN MARINERS

This is a prayer hymn for the close of worship; it asks for the Lord's blessing as we leave, and thanks God for the truth of the gospel in our lives. The tune is associated with the Roman Catholic "O Sanctissima" (which Sicilian sailors sang, according to tradition) and the German carol "O du Fröhliche."

How Vast the Benefits Divine   107

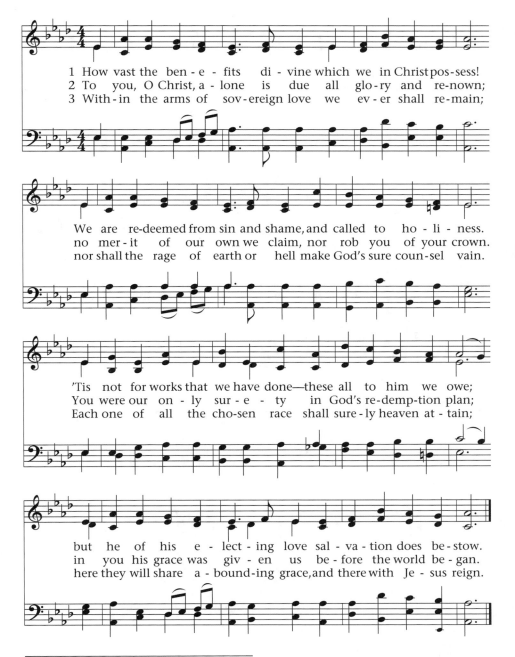

1 How vast the ben-e-fits di-vine which we in Christ pos-sess!
2 To you, O Christ, a-lone is due all glo-ry and re-nown;
3 With-in the arms of sov-ereign love we ev-er shall re-main;

We are re-deemed from sin and shame, and called to ho-li-ness.
no mer-it of our own we claim, nor rob you of your crown.
nor shall the rage of earth or hell make God's sure coun-sel vain.

'Tis not for works that we have done—these all to him we owe;
You were our on-ly sur-e-ty in God's re-demp-tion plan;
Each one of all the cho-sen race shall sure-ly heaven at-tain;

but he of his e-lect-ing love sal-va-tion does be-stow.
in you his grace was giv-en us be-fore the world be-gan.
here they will share a-bound-ing grace, and there with Je-sus reign.

Words: Augustus M. Toplady (1774), alt., P.D.
Music: Gottfried W. Fink (1842), P.D.

86 86 D
BETHLEHEM

An ardent Calvinist opponent of the Arminian Wesleys, Toplady wrote this text to express the essential points of the doctrine of redemption. The didactic outer stanzas surround a central stanza addressed to Christ. Fink's melody was set by Arthur Sullivan for "While Shepherds Watched Their Flocks," which resulted in the tune title.

108   I Know That My Redeemer Lives!

1 I know that my Re-deem-er lives! What joy this
2 He lives tri-um-phant from the grave; he lives e-
3 He lives to bless me with his love; he lives to
4 He lives, my kind, wise, heav-enly friend; he lives and

blest as-sur-ance gives! He lives, he lives, who
ter-nal-ly to save; he lives ex-alt-ed,
plead for me a-bove; he lives my hun-gry
loves me to the end; he lives, and while he

once was dead; he lives, my ev-er-liv-ing Head!
throned a-bove; he lives to rule his church in love.
soul to feed; he lives to help in time of need.
lives, I'll sing; he lives, my Proph-et, Priest, and King!

5 He lives, all glory to his name!
He lives, my Savior, still the same;
what joy this blest assurance gives:
I know that my Redeemer lives!

Words: Samuel Medley (1775), alt., P.D.
Music: John Hatton (1793), P.D.

88 88
DUKE STREET

In contrast to some of the other Easter hymns that stress the corporate and cosmic significance of Christ's resurrection, this text is a deeply personal confession like that in Job 19:25. Hatton is virtually anonymous, but his DUKE
STREET is a sturdy and much-loved melody for this text and for "Jesus Shall Reign" (77). The harmony comes
mostly from the *English Hymnal* (1906).

Rock of Ages, Cleft for Me   109

1 Rock of A - ges, cleft for me, let me hide my - self in thee.
2 Not the la - bors of my hands can ful - fill thy law's de-mands.
3 Noth-ing in my hand I bring, sim - ply to thy cross I cling;
4 While I draw this fleet-ing breath, when my eye - lids close in death,

Let the wa - ter and the blood, from thy riv - en side which flowed,
Could my zeal no res - pite know, could my tears for - ev - er flow,
na - ked, come to thee for dress, help-less, look to thee for grace.
when I soar to worlds un-known, see thee on thy judg-ment throne,

be of sin the dou - ble cure; cleanse me from its guilt and power.
all for sin could not a - tone; thou must save, and thou a - lone.
Foul, I to the foun - tain fly; wash me, Sav - ior, or I die.
Rock of A - ges, cleft for me, let me hide my - self in thee.

Words: Augustus M. Toplady (1776), P.D.
Music: Thomas Hastings (1830), P.D.

77 77 77
TOPLADY

Inspired by several Lord's Supper hymns by Charles Wesley, Toplady wrote "Rock of Ages" as a "living and dying prayer for [even] the holiest believer in the world." Hastings composed this tune for these words; some rhythmic differences in modern hymnals date back to Lowell Mason's use of this tune in his *Sabbath Hymn and Tune Book* (1859).

110 All Hail the Power of Jesus' Name!

1 All hail the power of Je - sus' name! Let an - gels pros-trate
2 Ye cho - sen seed of Is - rael's race, ye ran-somed from the
3 Let ev - ery kin - dred, ev - ery tribe on this ter - res - trial
4 Oh, that with yon - der sa - cred throng we at his feet may

fall, let an - gels pros - trate fall; bring forth the roy - al
fall, ye ran - somed from the fall, hail him who saves you
ball, on this ter - res - trial ball, to him all maj - es -
fall, we at his feet may fall! We'll join the ev - er -

Refrain

di - a - dem, and crown him,
by his grace,
ty as - cribe,
last - ing song, *and crown him, crown him, crown him, crown him,*

crown

crown him, crown him, crown him, and crown him Lord of all.

him, and crown him

Words: st. 1-3 Edward Perronet (1779), alt.; st. 4 John Rippon (1787), alt., P.D.
Music: James Ellor (1838), P.D.

86 86 with repeats
DIADEM

Originally titled "On the Resurrection, the Lord Is King," this coronation text affirms the cosmic reign of Christ.
The text is commonly sung to the anonymous fuguing tune MILES LANE, to the marching tune CORONATION
by Oliver Holden, or to the more elaborate choral setting provided here, DIADEM, by James Ellor.

How Firm a Foundation   111

1 How firm a foun-da-tion, you saints of the Lord,
2 "Fear not, I am with you, O be not dis-mayed,
3 "When through the deep wa-ters I call you to go,
4 "When through fi-ery tri-als your path-way shall lie,

is laid for your faith in his ex-cel-lent Word!
for I am your God and will still give you aid;
the riv-ers of sor-row shall not o-ver-flow,
my grace all-suf-fi-cient shall be your sup-ply;

What more can he say than to you he has said,
I'll strength-en you, help you, and cause you to stand,
for I will be with you in trou-ble to bless,
the flame shall not hurt you; I on-ly de-sign

to you who for re-fuge to Je-sus have fled?
up-held by my right-eous, om-nip-o-tent hand.
and sanc-ti-fy to you your deep-est dis-tress.
your dross to con-sume and your gold to re-fine.

5 "The soul that on Jesus
   has leaned for repose
 I will not, I will not desert to its foes;

that soul, though all hell
   should endeavor to shake,
 I'll never, no never, no never forsake!"

Words: John Rippon's *Selection of Hymns* (1787), alt.; based on Isaiah 43:1-5, P.D.   11 11 11 11
Music: Joseph Funk's *A Compilation of Genuine Church Music* (1832); harm. Dale Grotenhuis   FOUNDATION
   (1985) © 1987 Faith Alive Christian Resources

This is an anonymous paraphrase of a comforting prophecy in Isaiah, wed to a pentatonic melody that gained popularity for its inclusion in both *Southern Harmony* (1835) and *The Sacred Harp* (1844). It may be sung in canon, with successive entries at the equivalent of either one or two measures.

112 Angels We Have Heard on High

1 An - gels we have heard on high, sing - ing sweet-ly through the night,
2 Shep-herds, why this ju - bi - lee? Why these songs of hap - py cheer?
3 Come to Beth - le - hem and see him whose birth the an - gels sing;

and the moun-tains in re - ply, ech - o - ing their brave de - light.
What great bright-ness did you see? What glad tid - ings did you hear?
come, a - dore on bend-ed knee Christ the Lord, the new-born King.

Refrain

Glo - ri - a in ex-cel-sis De-o.

Glo - ri - a in ex-cel-sis De - o.

Words: French (18th c.); tr. *Crown of Jesus Music*, (1862), alt., P.D.
Music: French (18th c.); arr. Edward S. Barnes (1937), P.D.

77 77 with refrain
GLORIA

"Les Anges Dans Nos Campagnes" is a traditional noël from the Languedoc region of France. It was first published in 1855; its English translation appeared in a Roman Catholic collection, *Crown of Jesus Music*. The stirring refrain sings "Glory to God," without, unfortunately, affirming its complementary "peace on earth."

When Morning Gilds the Sky   113

1 When morn-ing gilds the sky,   our hearts a - wak - ing cry:
2 To   God, the Word on high,   the hosts of   an - gels cry:
3 Let   earth's wide cir - cle round   in   joy-ful   notes   re-sound:
4 Be   this, when day is   past,   of   all our thoughts the last:

May Je - sus Christ   be praised!   In   all   our work and   prayer
May Je - sus Christ   be praised!   Let   mor-tals too   up - raise
May Je - sus Christ   be praised!   Let   air   and sea and   sky
May Je - sus Christ   be praised!   The night be-comes as   day

we   ask his lov - ing   care: May Je - sus Christ be   praised!
their   voice in hymns of   praise: May Je - sus Christ be   praised!
from   depth to height re - ply: May Je - sus Christ be   praised!
when   from the heart we   say: May Je - sus Christ be   praised!

5 Then let us join to sing
to Christ, our loving King:
May Jesus Christ be praised!
Be this the eternal song
through all the ages long:
May Jesus Christ be praised!

Words: German (ca. 1800); tr. Edward Caswall (1858), alt., P.D.   666 D
Music: Joseph Barnby (1868), P.D.   LAUDES DOMINI

A Roman Catholic convert from Anglicanism, Caswall translated Latin and German hymns into English. The litany text of this praise hymn, like that of Psalm 136, invites a responsorial treatment that Barnby's tune does not promote. Yet text and tune have been inseparable since their first union in the 1868 *Appendix to Hymns Ancient and Modern*.

114 Angels from the Realms of Glory

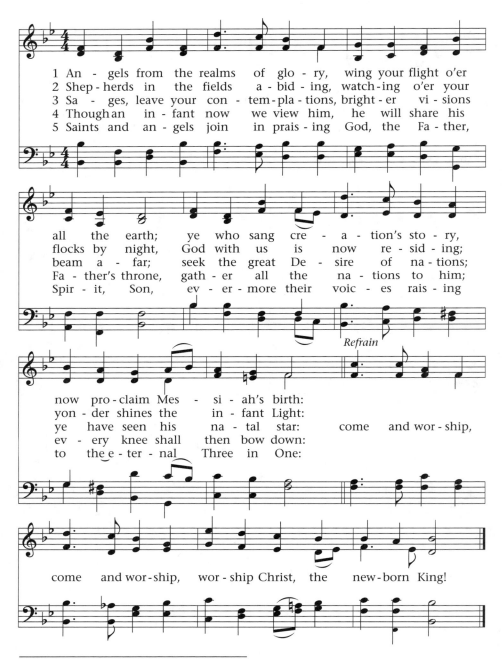

1 An - gels from the realms   of glo - ry,   wing your flight o'er
2 Shep - herds in   the fields   a - bid - ing, watch-ing   o'er your
3 Sa - ges, leave your con - tem-pla - tions, bright - er   vi - sions
4 Though an   in - fant now   we view him,   he   will share his
5 Saints and an - gels join   in prais - ing God, the   Fa - ther,

all   the   earth;   ye who sang   cre -   a - tion's sto - ry,
flocks by   night,   God with   us   is   now   re - sid - ing;
beam a - far;   seek the great De -   sire   of   na - tions;
Fa - ther's throne,   gath - er   all   the   na - tions to   him;
Spir - it,   Son,   ev - er - more their   voic - es   rais - ing

Refrain

now pro - claim Mes -   si - ah's birth:
yon - der shines the   in - fant Light:
ye   have seen his   na - tal   star: come   and wor - ship,
ev - ery knee shall   then bow down:
to   the e - ter - nal   Three   in   One:

come   and wor - ship,   wor - ship Christ,   the   new-born King!

Words: James Montgomery (1816), alt., P.D.
Music: Henry Smart (1867), P.D.

87 87 with refrain
REGENT SQUARE

A Moravian and a newspaper editor, Montgomery calls not only angels, shepherds, and wise men to worship "Christ the newborn King," but *all* nations and peoples to do so. Smart's REGENT SQUARE is a splendid tune with much melodic lift; the GLORIA tune associated with "Angels We Have Heard on High" (112) is a traditional alternate choice.

Come, You Disconsolate 115

1 Come, you dis- con- so-late, wher- e'er you lan- guish;
2 Joy of the des- o-late, light of the stray- ing,
3 Here see the bread of life; see wa- ters flow- ing

come to the mer- cy seat, fer- vent-ly kneel.
hope of the pen- i-tent, fade- less and pure!
forth from the throne of God, pure from a- bove.

Here bring your wound-ed hearts, here tell your an- guish;
Here speaks the Com- fort- er, in mer-cy say- ing,
Come to the feast pre-pared; come, ev- er know- ing

earth has no sor-rows that heaven can- not heal.
"Earth has no sor-rows that heaven can- not cure."
earth has no sor-rows but heaven can re- move.

Words: st. 1-2, Thomas Moore (1816); st. 1-2 rev. and st. 3, Thomas Hastings (1831), P.D.
Music: arr. from Samuel Webbe Sr. (1792), P.D.

11 10 11 10
CONSOLATION

This is an invitation hymn, originally titled "Relief in Prayer," asking sinners to come to Christ with their sorrow and find healing and comfort in him. With lyric sweetness and urgent rhythms, this melody is well-suited to the solace offered in this text.

116   Silent Night! Holy Night!

1 Silent night! Holy night! All is calm, all is bright round yon virgin mother and child! Holy infant, so tender and mild, sleep in heavenly peace! sleep in heavenly peace!

2 Silent night! Holy night! Son of God, source of light, now lies crying in Bethlehem's stall, tiny child, Creator of all, infant, Savior, and King! infant, Savior, and King!

3 Silent night! Holy night!
Shepherds quake at the sight
when they hear the angels sing
alleluia to the King.
Christ the Savior is born! *2x*

4 Silent night! Holy night!
Son of God, love's pure light
shines anew from your heavenly face,
greets the hour of redeeming grace,
Jesus, Lord, at your birth! *2x*

Words: st. 1, 3, 4 Joseph Mohr (1818); tr. John F. Young (1863), alt., P.D.;   irregular
   st. 2, Henrietta Ten Harmsel (1984); © 1987 Faith Alive Christian Resources
Music: Franz Gruber (1818), P.D.   STILLE NACHT

First written for a Christmas Eve service, Mohr's text evokes the night of Christ's birth with a mixture of sentiment and awe, made stronger theologically by Ten Harmsel's verse. Gruber's music, originally for voice and guitar, is in the gentle style of an Austrian slow waltz.

The Head That Once Was Crowned 117
with Thorns

1 The head that once was crowned with thorns is
2 The high - est place that heaven af - fords is
3 the joy of all who dwell a - bove, the
4 To them the cross with all its shame, with

crowned with glo - ry now; a roy - al di - a -
his, is his by right— the King of kings and
joy of all be - low, to whom he man - i -
all its grace, is given; their name, an ev - er -

dem a - dorns the might - y vic - tor's brow.
Lord of lords, and heaven's e - ter - nal Light;
fests his love and grants his Name to know.
last - ing name; their joy, the joy of heaven.

5 They suffer with their Lord below,
they reign with him above,
their profit and their joy to know
the mystery of his love.

6 The cross he bore is life and health,
though shame and death to him:
his people's hope, his people's wealth,
their everlasting theme.

Words: Thomas Kelly (1820), P.D.
Music: attr. Jeremiah Clark (1707), P.D.

86 86
ST. MAGNUS

Kelly's text takes in the grand sweep of Christ's death to his resurrection and ascension as a confession of faith and hope for all Christians. His words were united to ST. MAGNUS in the 1868 edition of *Hymns Ancient and Modern*. Note the stunning climax of an octave rise in the last phrase of this tune.

118 Ride On! Ride On in Majesty!

Unison

1 Ride on! Ride on in maj - es - ty! Hark! All the tribes ho-san-na cry: O Sav-ior meek, pur-sue thy road with palms and scat-tered gar-ments strowed.

2 Ride on! Ride on in maj - es - ty! In low-ly pomp ride on to die; O Christ, thy tri-umphs now be-gin o'er cap-tive death and con-quered sin.

3 Ride on! Ride on in maj - es - ty! The wing-ed squad-rons of the sky look down with sad and won-dering eyes to see the ap-proach-ing sac-ri-fice.

4 Ride on! Ride on in maj - es - ty! In low-ly pomp ride on to die; bow thy meek head to mor-tal pain, then take, O God, thy power, and reign.

Words: Henry H. Milman (1827), alt., P.D.
Music: Graham George (1930) © 1941, 1969 H. W. Gray Co., Inc., a division of Belwin Mills Publishing Corp.

88 88
THE KING'S MAJESTY

Milman's text combines a sense of tragedy and victory so appropriate to Palm Sunday. Modern hymnal editors have chosen a variety of tunes to fit this text. The one offered here, THE KING'S MAJESTY, was written specifically for these words, as an improvement over the match with WINCHESTER NEW, and is the only modern Canadian hymn-tune that has received wide acceptance in current hymnals.

Go to Dark Gethsemane 119

1 Go to dark Geth-sem-a-ne, all who feel the tempt-er's power; your Re-deem-er's con-flict see, watch with him one bit-ter hour: turn not from his griefs a-way— teach us, Lord, how we should pray.

2 Fol-low to the judg-ment hall, view the Lord of life ar-raigned. Oh, the worm-wood and the gall! Oh, the pangs his soul sus-tained! Shun not suf-fering, shame, or loss— help us, Lord, to bear our cross.

3 Cal-vary's mourn-ful moun-tain climb; there, a-dor-ing at his feet, mark the mir-a-cle of time, God's own sac-ri-fice com-plete: "It is fin-ished!" hear him cry— save us, Lord, when death draws nigh.

Words: James Montgomery (1825), alt., P.D.
Music: Richard Redhead (1853), P.D.

77 77 77
REDHEAD 76

Modern hymnals omit the original stanza about the resurrection, thereby letting us meditate on Christ's sorrow in the garden, his suffering on the cross, and his atoning death. This tune first appeared as No. 76 in Redhead's *Church Hymn Tunes* (1853), there associated with "Rock of Ages, Cleft for Me."

120 The First Noel

1 The first No-el the an-gel did say was to cer-tain poor
2 They look-ed up and saw a star shin-ing in the
3 And by the light of that same star three wise men
4 This star drew near to the north-west, o'er Beth-le-

shep-herds in fields as they lay; in fields where they lay,
east, be-yond them far, and to the earth it
came from coun-try far, to seek for a king was
hem it took its rest; and there it did both

keep-ing their sheep, on a cold win-ter's night that was so deep.
gave great light, and so it con-tin-ued both day and night.
their in-tent, and to fol-low the star wher-ev-er it went.
stop and stay right o-ver the place where Je-sus lay.

Refrain

No-el, No-el, No-el, No-el! Born is the King of Is-ra-el.

Words: trad. English carol; Davies Gilbert's *Some Ancient Christmas Carols* (1823), alt., P.D.
Music: trad. English melody; William Sandy's *Christmas Carols, Ancient and Modern* (1833);
harm. John Stainex (1871), P.D.

irregular
THE FIRST NOEL

5 Then entered in those wise men three,
   full reverently upon their knee,
   and offered there in his presence
   their gold, and myrrh, and frankincense.
   Refrain

6 Then let us all with one accord
   sing praises to our heavenly Lord,
   who has made heaven and earth of naught,
   and with his blood our life has bought.
   Refrain

Not unlike the art on many Christmas cards, this British carol unabashedly fuses the shepherds, the star, and the Magi. Regardless of that error and the high melody line, it is a popular carol sung with great sentiment in many Christmas and Epiphany services.

121 In the Cross of Christ I Glory

1 In the cross of Christ I glo-ry, tow-ering o'er the
2 When the woes of life o'er-take me, hopes de-ceive and
3 When the sun of bliss is beam-ing light and love up-
4 Bane and bless-ing, pain and plea-sure, by the cross are

wrecks of time; all the light of sa - cred
fears an - noy, nev - er shall the cross for -
on my way, from the cross the ra - diance,
sanc - ti - fied; peace is there that knows no

sto - ry gath - ers round its head sub - lime.
sake me; lo! it glows with peace and joy.
stream-ing, adds more lus - ter to the day.
mea - sure, joys that through all time a - bide.

Words: John Bowring (1825), P.D.
Music: Ithamar Conkey (1851), P.D.

87 87
RATHBUN

In some ways similar to "Lift High the Cross" (162) in not being a veneration of the cross, Bowring's text explains for all Christians the meaning of Paul's confession, "May I never boast except in the cross of our Lord Jesus Christ" (Gal. 6:14). Conkey wrote this tune for Bowring's text following a frustrating Sunday morning when only one soprano showed up for his church choir; the tune is named for that soprano, Beriah Rathbun.

Holy, Holy, Holy! Lord God Almighty 122

1 Ho-ly, ho-ly, ho-ly! Lord_____ God Al-might-y!
2 Ho-ly, ho-ly, ho-ly! All the saints a-dore thee,
3 Ho-ly, ho-ly, ho-ly! Though the dark-ness hide thee,
4 Ho-ly, ho-ly, ho-ly! Lord_____ God Al-might-y!

Ear - ly in the morn - ing our song shall rise to thee;
cast - ing down their gold-en crowns a - round the glass-y sea;
though the eye made blind by sin thy glo - ry may not see,
All thy works shall praise thy name, in earth and sky and sea;

ho - ly, ho - ly, ho - ly! mer - ci - ful and might - y,
cher-u - bim and ser - a-phim fall - ing down be - fore thee,
on - ly thou art ho - ly; there is none be - side thee,
ho - ly, ho - ly, ho - ly! mer - ci - ful and might - y,

God in three per - sons, bless - ed Trin - i - ty!
who wert and art and ev - er - more shalt be.
per - fect in power, in love, and pu - ri - ty.
God in three per - sons, bless - ed Trin - i - ty!

Words: Reginald Heber (1827), alt., P.D.
Music: John B. Dykes (1861), P.D.

11 12 12 10
NICEA

Inspired by Revelation 4:6-11, Heber wrote this cosmic text about the great majesty of the Triune God. It was published posthumously in Heber's *Hymns* (1827), a hymnal that deliberately grouped hymns according to the season of the church year. Dykes' music has been wedded inseparably to this text ever since its first inclusion in *Hymns Ancient and Modern* (1861).

123 O Worship the King

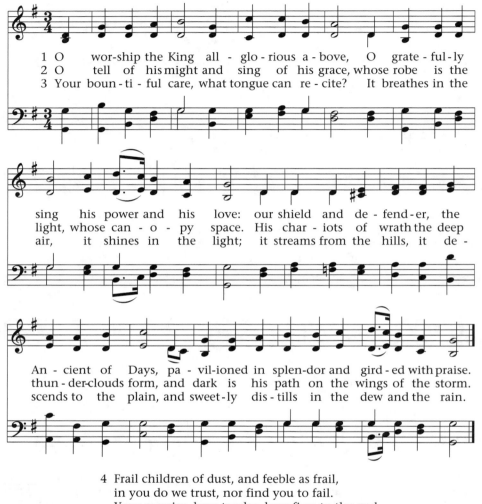

1 O wor-ship the King all - glo - rious a - bove, O grate - ful-ly
2 O tell of his might and sing of his grace, whose robe is the
3 Your boun - ti - ful care, what tongue can re - cite? It breathes in the

sing his power and his love: our shield and de - fend-er, the
light, whose can - o - py space. His char - iots of wrath the deep
air, it shines in the light; it streams from the hills, it de -

An - cient of Days, pa - vil-ioned in splen-dor and gird - ed with praise.
thun - der-clouds form, and dark is his path on the wings of the storm.
scends to the plain, and sweet-ly dis - tills in the dew and the rain.

4 Frail children of dust, and feeble as frail,
in you do we trust, nor find you to fail.
Your mercies, how tender, how firm to the end,
our Maker, Defender, Redeemer, and Friend!

5 O measureless Might, unchangeable Love,
whom angels delight to worship above!
Your ransomed creation, with glory ablaze,
in true adoration shall sing to your praise!

Words: Robert Grant (1833), alt.; based on Psalm 104, P.D.
Music: Joseph M. Kraus (c. 1785), in William Gardiner's *Sacred Melodies* (1815), alt., P.D.

10 10 11 11
LYONS

Grant's text is a meditation on the creation and providence themes found in Psalm 104. Kraus composed the tune as a theme and variations piece for piano, with a violin part added some twenty years later by an unknown "G. Haydn" (not the famous Franz J. Haydn nor his brother Johann M. Haydn). The melody appears as a hymn-tune in William Gardiner's *Sacred Melodies* (1815); the pedal point in the third phrase has been reharmonized by Bert Polman.

Just as I Am, without One Plea   124

1 Just as I am, with-out one plea, but that thy blood was
2 Just as I am, and wait-ing not to rid my soul of
3 Just as I am, though tossed a-bout with man-y a con-flict,
4 Just as I am, thou wilt re-ceive, wilt wel-come, par-don,

shed for me, and that thou bidd'st me come to thee,
one dark blot, to thee, whose blood can cleanse each spot,
man-y a doubt, fight-ings and fears with-in, with-out,
cleanse, re-lieve; be-cause thy prom-ise I be-lieve,

O Lamb of God, I come, I come.

Words: Charlotte Elliott (1836), P.D.
Music: William B. Bradbury (1849), P.D.

88 88
WOODWORTH

Elliott's text was the autobiographical memorial of her conversion to Christ. Bradbury added an extra "I come" to the final phrase to fit this text to his new tune. The marriage of text and tune was cemented through frequent use in the Moody-Sankey crusades in the late nineteenth century, and more recently as a much-loved invitation hymn in Billy Graham crusades.

125 My Hope Is Built on Nothing Less

1 My hope is built on noth-ing less than Je-sus' blood and
2 When dark-ness veils his love-ly face, I rest on his un-
3 His oath, his cov-e-nant, his blood sup-port me in the
4 When he shall come with trum-pet sound, oh, may I then in

righ-teous-ness; no mer-it of my own I claim but
chang-ing grace; in ev-ery high and storm-y gale, my
rag-ing flood; when ev-ery earth-ly prop gives way, he
him be found, clothed in his righ-teous-ness a-lone, re-

Refrain

whol-ly lean on Je-sus' name.
an-chor holds with-in the veil. On Christ the sol-id rock I stand;
then is all my hope and stay.
deemed to stand be-fore the throne!

all oth-er ground is sink-ing sand, all oth-er ground is sink-ing sand.

Words: Edward Mote (1834), P.D.
Music: William B. Bradbury (1863), P.D.

88 88 with refrain
THE SOLID ROCK

Mote is among the first to use the term "gospel hymn," and this text of his sets out the pattern used by many later gospel hymns: two couplets with related ideas in the stanzas and then a refrain. In this case the text draws on powerful imagery from Jesus' parable of building a house on rock rather than sand. Sometimes known as "the father of Sunday school hymnody," Bradbury composed the tune specifically for this text while the United States was suffering through its Civil War.

Savior, Like a Shepherd Lead Us   126

1 Sa-vior, like a shep-herd lead us; much we need your ten-der care.
2 We are yours; in love be-friend us, be the guard-ian of our way.

In your pleas - ant pas-tures feed us, for our use your fold pre-pare.
Keep your flock, from sin de - fend us, seek us when we go a-stray.

Bless-ed Je-sus, bless-ed Je-sus, you have bought us, we are yours.
Bless-ed Je-sus, bless-ed Je-sus, hear us chil - dren when they pray.

Bless-ed Je-sus, bless-ed Je-sus, you have bought us, we are yours.
Bless-ed Je-sus, bless-ed Je-sus, hear us chil - dren when they pray.

3 You have promised to receive us,
poor and sinful though we be;
you have mercy to relieve us,
grace to cleanse, and power to free.
[Blessed Jesus, blessed Jesus,
early let us turn to you. *2x*]

4 Early let us seek your favor,
early let us do your will;
blessed Lord and only Savior,
with your love our spirits fill.
[Blessed Jesus, blessed Jesus,
you have loved us, love us still. *2x*]

Words: Dorothy Thrupp's *Hymns for the Young*, 4th ed., (1836), alt., P.D.
Music: William B. Bradbury (1859), P.D.

87 87 D
BRADBURY

Inspired by Psalm 23 and Jesus' parable of the good shepherd, this anonymous text was set to music by Bradbury and published in one of his many Sunday school hymnals. The hymn gained popularity when Moody and Sankey used it in their crusades.

127 Come, You Thankful People, Come

1 Come, you thank-ful peo-ple, come, praise the song of har-vest home;
2 All the world is God's own field, fruit un-to his praise to yield;
3 For the Lord our God shall come and shall take his har-vest home;
4 E-ven so, Lord, quick-ly come to your fi-nal har-vest home;

all is safe-ly gath-ered in ere the win-ter storms be-gin;
wheat and weeds to-geth-er sown, un-to joy or sor-row grown:
he him-self in that great day all of-fense shall take a-way,
gath-er all your peo-ple in, free from sor-row, free from sin

God, our Mak-er, does pro-vide for our needs to be sup-plied;
first the blade and then the ear, then the full corn shall ap-pear;
give his an-gels charge at last in the fire the weeds to cast,
there, for-ev-er pu-ri-fied, in your pres-ence to a-bide;

come, with all his peo-ple come, raise the song of har-vest home.
Lord of har-vest, grant that we whole-some grain and pure may be.
but the fruit-ful ears to store in his gar-ner ev-er-more.
come, with all your an-gels come, raise the glo-rious har-vest home.

Words: Henry Alford (1844), alt., P.D.
Music: George J. Elvey (1858), P.D.

77 77 D
ST. GEORGE'S WINDSOR

Written for harvest festivals, this text turns from agricultural harvest and parable themes (seed, wheat, tares) to eschatology, to a "glorious harvest home." Elvey's tune has been associated with Alford's text since their first union in *Hymns Ancient and Modern* (1861).

I Heard the Voice of Jesus Say   128

1 I heard the voice of Je-sus say, "Come un-to me and rest;
2 I heard the voice of Je-sus say, "Be-hold, I free-ly give
3 I heard the voice of Je-sus say, "I am this dark world's lift;

lay down, thou wea-ry one, lay down thy head up-on my breast."
the liv-ing wa-ter; thirs-ty one, stoop down and drink and live."
look un-to me, thy morn shall rise, and all thy day be bright."

I came to Je-sus as I was, so wea-ry, worn, and sad;
I came to Je-sus and I drank of that life-giv-ing stream;
I looked to Je-sus and I found in him my star, my sun;

I found in him a rest-ing place, and he has made me glad.
my thirst was quenched, my soul re-vived, and now I live in him.
and in that light of life I'll walk till trav-eling days are done.

Words: Horatius Bonar (1946), P.D.   86 86 D
Music: trad. English and Irish melody, *English County Songs* (1893); adapt. and harm.   KINGSFOLD
    Ralph Vaughen Williams (1906), P.D.

Written as a children's hymn, Bonar's text juxtaposes quotations from Jesus with a Christian's personal responses of finding rest, nurture, and light in Christ. Vaughan Williams arranged the traditional modal melody for use with Bonar's text in the *English Hymnal* (1906). The text suggests some use of responsive or antiphonal singing between the first and second part of each stanza.

129 Abide with Me

1 A - bide with me: fast falls the e - ven - tide; the dark-ness
2 Swift to its close ebbs out life's lit - tle day; earth's joys grow
3 I need your pres - ence ev - ery pass-ing hour. What but your

deep-ens; Lord, with me a - bide. When oth - er help-ers fail and
dim, its glo - ries pass a - way. Change and de - cay in all a -
grace can foil the tempt-er's power? Who like your-self my guide and

com - forts flee, Help of the help - less, O a - bide with me.
round I see. O Lord who chang - es not, a - bide with me.
strength can be? Through cloud and sun-shine, O a - bide with me.

4 I fear no foe with you at hand to bless,
   though ills have weight, and tears their bitterness.
   Where is death's sting? Where, grave, your victory?
   I triumph still, if you abide with me.

5 Hold now your Word before my closing eyes.
   Shine through the gloom and point me to the skies.
   Heaven's morning breaks and earth's vain shadows flee;
   in life, in death, O Lord, abide with me.

Words: Henry F. Lyte (1847), alt., P.D.
Music: William H. Monk (1861), P.D.

10 10 10 10
EVENTIDE

Though inspired by Luke 24:29, Lyte's hymn develops "evening" as an extended metaphor for the close of life. Stanza 4 originally contained the line "Ills have no weight and tears no bitterness," which the editors of the *Psalter Hymnal* (1987) changed to reflect the realism of Psalm 23:4. The union of this text and tune was made by the editors of *Hymns Ancient and Modern* (1861).

All Things Bright and Beautiful 130

Refrain
Unison

All things bright and beau-ti-ful, all crea-tures great and small,

all things wise and won-der-ful— the Lord God made them all.

1 Each lit - tle flower that o - pens, each lit - tle bird that sings—
2 The pur - ple-head - ed moun-tain, the riv - er run-ning by,
3 The cold wind in the win - ter, the pleas - ant sum - mer sun,
4 He gave us eyes to see them, and lips that we might tell

To Refrain

he made their glow-ing col - ors, he made their ti - ny wings.
the sun - set, and the morn - ing that bright-ens up the sky.
the ripe fruits in the gar - den—he made them ev - ery one.
how great is God Al - might - y, who has made all things well.

Words: Cecil F. Alexander (1848), P.D.
Music: *The Dancing Master* (1686); harm. John Worst (1974), alt. © 1987 Faith Alive
Christian Resources

76 76 with refrain
ROYAL OAK

This is the hymn text that Alexander wrote for children to explain the Apostles' Creed article on God as the "maker of heaven and earth." The ROYAL OAK tune features an antiphon—a refrain that begins the song and then recurs as any refrain would do.

131 Once in Royal David's City

1 Once in roy-al Da-vid's cit-y stood a low-ly cat-tle shed,
2 He came down to earth from heav-en who is God and Lord of all;
3 For he is our child-hood's pat-tern, day by day like us he grew;

where a moth-er laid her ba-by in a man-ger for his bed:
and his shel-ter was a sta-ble and his cra-dle was a stall:
he was lit-tle, weak, and help-less, tears and smiles like us he knew:

Ma-ry was that moth-er mild, Je-sus Christ, her lit-tle child.
with the poor, and meek, and low-ly lived on earth our Sav-ior ho-ly.
and he feels for all our sad-ness, and he shares in all our glad-ness.

4 And our eyes at last shall see him,
  through his own redeeming love,
  for that child, so dear and gentle,
  is our Lord in heaven above:
  and he leads his children on
  to the place where he has gone.

5 Not in that poor lowly stable
  with the oxen standing by
  we shall see him, but in heaven,
  set at God's right hand on high:
  there his children gather round
  bright like stars, with glory crowned.

Words: Cecil F. Alexander (1848), P.D.
Music: Henry J. Gauntlett (1849), P.D.

87 87 77
IRBY

Alexander wrote this text to explain to children the Apostles' Creed confession about Jesus "who was conceived by the Holy Spirit, born of the Virgin Mary," but she actually set her text in the larger framework of the history of salvation. Gauntlett's graceful tune, IRBY, was written for this text and their union has prevailed in all modern hymnals.

My God, How Wonderful You Are   132

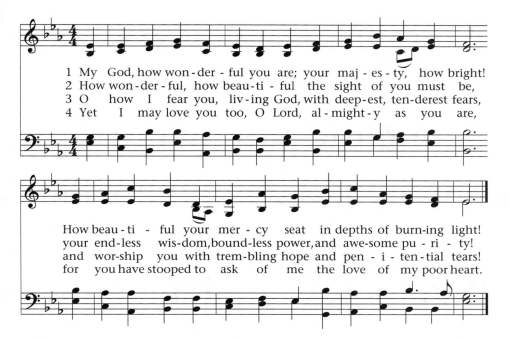

1 My God, how won-der-ful you are; your maj-es-ty, how bright!
2 How won-der-ful, how beau-ti-ful the sight of you must be,
3 O how I fear you, liv-ing God, with deep-est, ten-derest fears,
4 Yet I may love you too, O Lord, al-might-y as you are,

How beau-ti-ful your mer-cy seat in depths of burn-ing light!
your end-less wis-dom, bound-less power, and awe-some pu-ri-ty!
and wor-ship you with trem-bling hope and pen-i-ten-tial tears!
for you have stooped to ask of me the love of my poor heart.

5 No earthly father loves like you,
   no mother half so mild
   bears and forbears as you have done
   with me, your sinful child.

6 Father of Jesus, Love divine,
   great King upon your throne,
   what joy to see you as you are
   and worship you alone!

Words: Frederick W. Faber (1849), alt., P.D.
Music: Thomas Turton (1860), P.D.

86 86
ST. ETHELDREDA

Written after he converted from the Church of England to Roman Catholicism, Faber penned this text to extol the awesome God we worship. Turton was Bishop of Ely, where Etheldreda (630-679) was venerated as Queen of Northumbria. His simple, psalmtune-like melody is hardly a match, however, for the grandeur of Faber's words.

133 Crown Him with Many Crowns

1 Crown him with man-y crowns, the Lamb up - on his throne, while
2 Crown him the Lord of life, tri - um-phant o'er the grave, who
3 Crown him the Lord of peace; his king-dom is at hand. From

heaven's e - ter - nal an - them drowns all mu - sic but its own!
rose vic - to - rious from the strife for those he came to save.
pole to pole let war - fare cease and Christ rule ev - ery land!

A - wake, my soul, and sing of him who died to be your
His glo - ries now we sing who died and reigns on high; he
All hail, Re-deem-er, hail, for you have died for me. Your

Sav - ior and your match-less King through all e - ter - ni - ty.
died, e - ter - nal life to bring, and lives that death may die.
praise shall nev - er, nev - er fail through-out e - ter - ni - ty.

Words: st. 1, 3, Matthew Bridges (1851); st. 2, Godfrey Thring (1874); alt., P.D.
Music: George J. Elvey (1868), P.D.

86 68 D
DIADEMATA

This hymn is a composite of two texts, both inspired by Revelation 19:12, that celebrate Christ's victory over sin and death and his rule in the world. Elvey's lively tune was composed for Bridges' text and first published in the appendix of *Hymns Ancient and Modern* (1868).

Jesus Calls Us, o'er the Tumult   134

1 Je - sus calls us, o'er the tu - mult of our
2 As of old Saint An - drew heard it by the
3 Je - sus calls us from the wor - ship of the
4 In our joys and in our sor - rows, days of

life's wild, rest - less sea, day by day his clear voice
Gal - i - le - an lake, turned from home and toil and
vain world's gold - en store, from each i - dol that would
toil and hours of ease, still he calls, in cares and

sound - ing, say - ing, "Chris - tian, fol - low me":
kin - dred, leav - ing all for Je - sus' sake.
keep us, say - ing, "Chris - tian, love me more."
pleas - ures, "Chris-tian, love me more than these."

5 Jesus calls us! By your mercy,
  Savior, may we hear your call,
  give our hearts to your obedience,
  serve and love you best of all.

Words: Cecil F. Alexander (1852), P.D.
Music: William H. Jude (1887), P.D.

87 87
GALILEE

Alexander wrote her text for St. Andrew's Day, for which the appointed gospel reading concerns Christ's calling of Peter and Andrew (Matt. 4:18-20). It is still a popular hymn about Jesus' call for us to follow him. Jude's tune GALILEE was written for this text.

135 Built on the Rock

1 Built on the Rock, the church shall stand even when steeples are
2 Not in a temple made with hands God the Almighty is
3 We are God's house of living stones, built for his own habi-

fall - ing; Christ builds his church in every land;
dwell - ing; high in the heavens his temple stands,
ta - tion; he fills our hearts, his humble thrones,

bells still are chim-ing and call - ing, call-ing the
all earth-ly tem-ples ex-cel - ling. Yet he who
grant-ing us life and sal-va - tion. Yet to this

young and old to rest, call-ing the souls of
dwells in heaven a-bove choos-es to live with
place, an earth-ly frame, we come with thanks to

those dis-tressed, long-ing for life ev-er-last - ing.
us in love, mak-ing our bod-ies his tem - ple.
praise his name; God grants his peo-ple true bless - ing.

Words: Nikolai Grundtvig (1854); tr. Carl Doving (1909), P.D.   88 88 888
Music: Ludwig M. Lindeman (1840), P.D.   KIRKEN

Drawing on biblical texts, this hymn emphasizes that the Christian church is not a building but a people who
are indwelt by God and founded on Christ. United with this rugged tune, this hymn is a great favorite among
Scandinavian Christians, second only to Luther's "A Mighty Fortress."

Children of the Heavenly Father   136

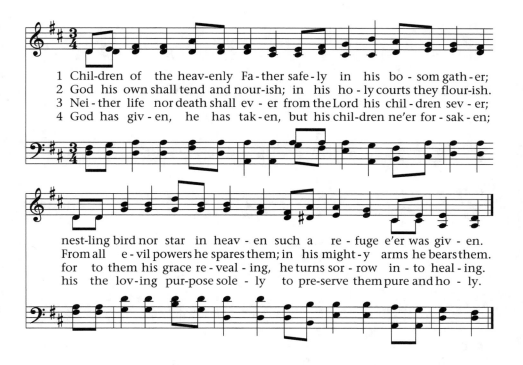

1 Chil-dren of the heav-enly Fa-ther safe-ly in his bo - som gath-er;
2 God his own shall tend and nour-ish; in his ho - ly courts they flour-ish.
3 Nei - ther life nor death shall ev - er from the Lord his chil - dren sev - er;
4 God has giv - en, he has tak-en, but his chil-dren ne'er for - sak-en;

nest-ling bird nor star in heav - en such a   re - fuge e'er was giv - en.
From all   e - vil powers he spares them; in his might - y   arms he bears them.
for   to them his grace re - veal - ing,   he turns sor - row   in - to heal-ing.
his   the lov-ing pur-pose sole - ly   to pre-serve them pure and ho - ly.

Words: Caroline V. Sandell Berg (1855); tr. Ernest W. Olson (1925), alt. © 1978 Board of   88 88
Publication of the Lutheran Church in America (admin. Augsburg Fortess)
Music: Swedish folk melody: *Lofsånger och andeliga wisor* (1873), P.D.   TRYGGARE KAN INGEN VARA

Better known as "Lina Sandell," who penned hundreds of gospel hymns, Berg wrote this text to confess a humble
trust in God's providence that prevails even when "sorrow" doesn't immediately turn to "healing" (st. 3).

137 How Bright Appears the Morning Star

1 How bright ap - pears the Morn-ing Star, with mer - cy beam-ing
2 Though cir - cled by the hosts on high, he deigned to cast a
3 Re - joice, O heavens, and earth, re - ply; with praise, O sin - ners,

from a - far; the host of heaven re - joic - es.
pit - ying eye up - on his help - less crea - ture.
fill the sky for this, his in - car - na - tion.

O Right-eous Branch, O Jes - se's Rod, the Son of Man and
The whole cre - a - tion's head and Lord, by high-est ser - a -
In - car - nate God, put forth your power, ride on, ride on, great

Son of God! We too will lift our voic - es:
phim a - dored, as - sumed our ver - y na - ture;
Con - quer - or, till all know your sal - va - tion.

Words: William Mercer (1859), P.D.
Music: Philipp Nicolai (1599); adapt. and harm. Johann S. Bach (1685-1750), P.D.

887 887 48 48
WIE SCHÖN LEUCHTET

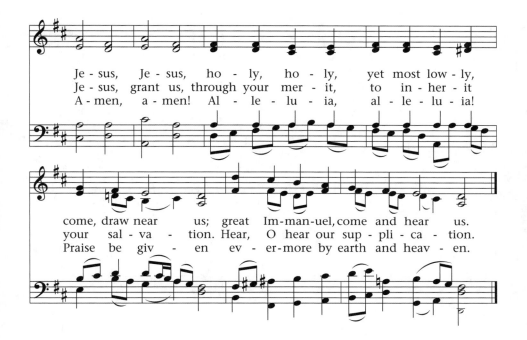

Je - sus, Je - sus, ho - ly, ho - ly, yet most low - ly,
Je - sus, grant us, through your mer - it, to in - her - it
A - men, a - men! Al - le - lu - ia, al - le - lu - ia!

come, draw near us; great Im-man-uel, come and hear us.
your sal - va - tion. Hear, O hear our sup - pli - ca - tion.
Praise be giv - en ev - er-more by earth and heav - en.

This is an original text by Mercer, written for Epiphany, and intended for use with the famous chorale tune of Nicolai. It is not a translation of Nicolai's text, though Mercer does borrow his opening line from Nicolai. The musical setting by Bach is isorhythmic (all the same rhythms): we lose the rhythmic interest of the original tune, but we gain the rich harmonization.

138 As with Gladness Men of Old

1 As with glad-ness men of old did the guid-ing star be-hold,
2 As with joy-ful steps they sped to that low-ly in-fant bed,
3 As they of-fered gifts most rare at that cra-dle plain and bare,

as with joy they hailed its light, lead - ing on - ward,
there to bend the knee be - fore Christ, whom heaven and
so may we with ho - ly joy, pure and free from

beam - ing bright; so, most gra - cious Lord, may
earth a - dore; so may we with will - ing
sin's al - loy, all our cost - liest trea - sures

we ev - er - more your splen - dor see.
feet ev - er seek your mer - cy seat.
bring, Christ, to you, our heav - enly King.

4 Holy Jesus, every day
keep us in the narrow way,
and when mortal things are past,
bring our ransomed lives at last
where they need no star to guide,
where no clouds your glory hide.

5 In that glorious city bright
none shall need created light;
you its light, its joy, its crown,
you its sun which goes not down;
there forever may we sing
alleluias to our King!

Words: William C. Dix (1860), alt., P.D.
Music: Conrad Kocher (1838); adapt. William H. Monk (1861), P.D.

77 77 77
DIX

This text by Dix, an insurance executive, was inspired by the Epiphany gospel of Matthew 1:1-11. He offers the pattern "as the wise men—so may we," and ultimately invites us to finish our journey in the "glory where Christ is the light." Monk revised Kocher's melody for use in *Hymns Ancient and Modern*, in which this text and tune were united for the first time—a union Dix never liked.

Not What My Hands Have Done   139

1 Not what my hands have done can save my guilt-y soul;
2 Your voice a-lone, O Lord, can speak to me of grace;
3 I praise the Christ of God; I rest on love di-vine;

not what my toil-ing flesh has borne can make my spir-it whole.
your power a-lone, O Son of God, can all my sin e-rase.
and with un-fal-tering lip and heart I call this Sav-ior mine.

Not what I feel or do can give me peace with God; not
No oth-er work but yours, no oth-er blood will do; no
My Lord has saved my life and free-ly par-don gives; I

all my prayers and sighs and tears can bear my aw-ful load.
strength but that which is di-vine can bear me safe-ly through.
love be-cause he first loved me, I live be-cause he lives.

Words: Horatius Bonar (1861), alt., P.D.   66 86 D
Music: George William Martin (1862), P.D.   LEOMINSTER

The Scottish preacher and hymn author Bonar wrote this text in part to side with John Calvin in the Calvin/
Arminius controversy about human freedom and divine election. Martin's tune develops from its dull opening
line to a much more dramatic melody in the later phrases.

140 Songs of Thankfulness and Praise

1 Songs of thank-ful-ness and praise, Je - sus, Lord, to you we raise,
2 Man - i - fest at Jor - dan's stream, Proph-et, Priest, and King su-preme;
3 Man - i - fest in mak - ing whole pal - sied limbs and faint-ing soul;

man - i - fest-ed by the star to the sa - ges from a - far;
and at Ca-na, wed - ding guest, in your God-head man - i - fest,
man - i - fest in val - iant fight, quell-ing all the dev-il's might;

Branch of roy - al Da-vid's stem, in your birth at Beth - le-hem;
you re-vealed your power di - vine, chang-ing wa - ter in - to wine;
man - i - fest in gra-cious will, ev - er bring-ing good from ill;

Refrain

"You are Christ," by us con-fessed— God in flesh made man-i-fest.

Words: Christopher Wordsworth (1862), alt., P.D.
Music: Jakob Hintze (1678); harm. after Johann S. Bach (1685-1750), P.D.

77 77 D
SALZBURG

Wordsworth's text is a didactic summary of the various manifestations of Christ that are the themes of the Epiphany season of the church year. Hintze is best known as the editor of the later versions of Crüger's famous *Praxis Pietatis Melica,* in whose 19th edition this tune is found.

There's a Wideness in God's Mercy   141

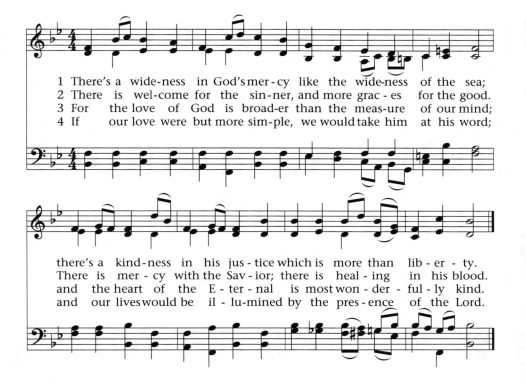

1 There's a wide-ness in God's mer-cy like the wide-ness of the sea;
2 There is wel-come for the sin-ner, and more grac-es for the good.
3 For the love of God is broad-er than the meas-ure of our mind;
4 If our love were but more sim-ple, we would take him at his word;

there's a kind-ness in his jus-tice which is more than lib-er-ty.
There is mer-cy with the Sav-ior; there is heal-ing in his blood.
and the heart of the E-ter-nal is most won-der-ful-ly kind.
and our lives would be il-lu-mined by the pres-ence of the Lord.

Words: Frederick W. Faber (1862), P.D.
Music: Lizzie S. Tourjée (1877), P.D.

87 87
WELLESLEY

Written after his conversion to Roman Catholicism, these select stanzas from Faber's longer text exhort us to grasp the cosmic scope of God's mercy. Tourjée composed the tune for her high school graduation, but it was wed with Faber's text in the *Methodist Hymnal* (1878) for which Tourjeé's father was an editor.

142 Fill Thou My Life, O Lord, My God

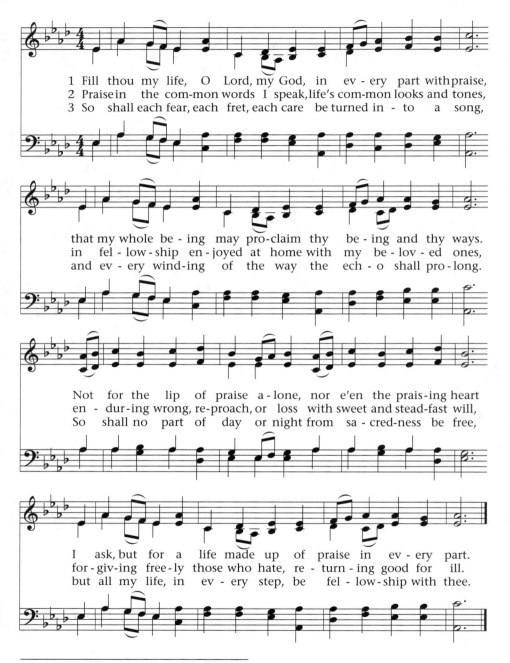

1 Fill thou my life, O Lord, my God, in ev - ery part with praise,
2 Praise in the com-mon words I speak, life's com-mon looks and tones,
3 So shall each fear, each fret, each care be turned in - to a song,

that my whole be - ing may pro-claim thy be - ing and thy ways.
in fel - low-ship en - joyed at home with my be - lov - ed ones,
and ev - ery wind-ing of the way the ech - o shall pro - long.

Not for the lip of praise a - lone, nor e'en the prais-ing heart
en - dur-ing wrong, re-proach, or loss with sweet and stead-fast will,
So shall no part of day or night from sa - cred-ness be free,

I ask, but for a life made up of praise in ev - ery part.
for - giv-ing free - ly those who hate, re - turn - ing good for ill.
but all my life, in ev - ery step, be fel - low-ship with thee.

Words: Horatius Bonar (1863), alt., P.D.
Music: *Gesangbuch der Herzogl*, Würtemburg (1784), P.D.

86 86 D
ELLACOMBE

This excerpt from Bonar's poem "Life's Praise" is a teaching hymn that encourages us to see all of life as a doxology to God. Though variants are found earlier in the eighteenth century, this cheerful tune comes from a chapel hymnal used at the Roman Catholic court of the Duke of Würtemberg; it gained popularity from its inclusion in the 1868 *Appendix to Hymns Ancient and Modern*.

For the Beauty of the Earth   143

1 For the beau-ty of the earth, for the glo-ry of the skies,
2 For the won-der of each hour of the day and of the night,
3 For the joy of hu-man love, broth-er, sis-ter, par-ent, child,
4 For your-self, best gift di-vine, to the world so free-ly given,

for the love which from our birth o-ver and a-round us lies,
hill and vale and tree and flower, sun and moon and stars of light,
friends on earth, and friends a-bove, for all gen-tle thoughts and mild,
a - gent of God's grand de-sign: peace on earth and joy in heaven.

Refrain

Christ, our Lord, to you we raise this, our hymn of grate-ful praise.

Words: Folliott S. Pierpont (1864), alt., P.D.
Music: Conrad Kocher (1838); adapt. William H. Monk (1861), P.D.

77 77 77
DIX

Originally "Christ, our God, to thee we raise this our sacrifice of praise," the refrain was changed from its eucharistic intent to a hymn of general thanksgiving for creation, families, and God's greatest gift, Jesus. The popularity of Monk's revision of Kocher's melody for use in *Hymns Ancient and Modern* led to the use of DIX for Pierpont's text.

144   For All the Saints

Unison

1 For all the saints who from their la - bors rest,
2 You were their rock, their for - tress, and their might;
3 May all your sol - diers, faith-ful, true, and bold,

who to the world by faith their Lord con - fessed,
you, Lord, their cap - tain in the well-fought fight,
fight as the saints who no - bly fought of old,

your name, O Je - sus, be for - ev - er blest.
and in the dark - ness drear, their one true light.
and win with them the vic - tor's crown of gold.

Al - le - lu - ia, al - le - lu - ia!

Words: William W. How (1864), alt., P.D.
Music: Ralph Vaughan Williams (1906), P.D.

10 10 10 with alleluias
SINE NOMINE

Harmony

4 O blest com - mu - nion, fel - low - ship di - vine!
5 And when the strife is fierce, the war - fare long,

We fee - bly strug - gle, they in glo - ry shine; yet
far off we hear the dis - tant tri - umph song; and

all are one with - in your great de - sign.
hearts are brave a - gain, and arms are strong.

Al - le - lu - ia, al - le - lu - ia!

Return to Unison

6 But then there breaks
    a yet more glorious day:
  the saints triumphant
    rise in bright array;
  the King of glory passes on his way.
  Alleluia, alleluia!

7 From earth's wide bounds,
    from ocean's farthest coast,
  through gates of pearl streams
    in the countless host,
  singing to Father, Son, and Holy Ghost:
  Alleluia, alleluia!

Inspired by Hebrews 12:1, How's grand text originally included stanzas for apostles, evangelists, and martyrs.
Vaughan Williams composed the tune (with its energetic "walking bass") for this text and published them together
in the *English Hymnal* (1906).

145 Day by Day

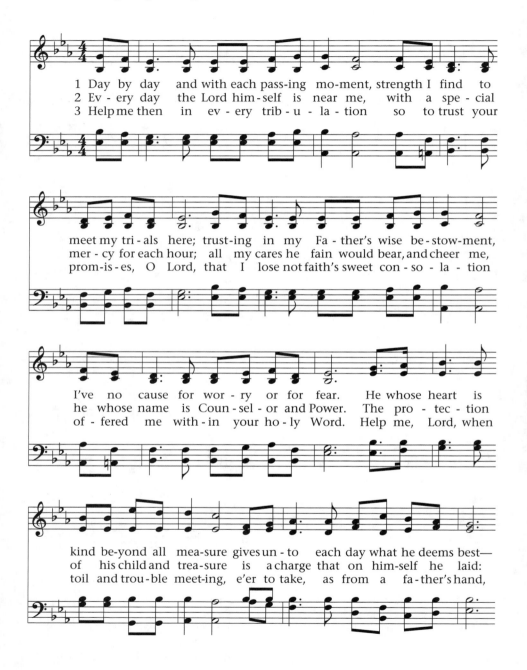

1 Day by day and with each pass-ing mo-ment, strength I find to
2 Ev - ery day the Lord him-self is near me, with a spe - cial
3 Help me then in ev - ery trib - u - la - tion so to trust your

meet my tri - als here; trust-ing in my Fa - ther's wise be-stow-ment,
mer - cy for each hour; all my cares he fain would bear, and cheer me,
prom-is - es, O Lord, that I lose not faith's sweet con - so - la - tion

I've no cause for wor - ry or for fear. He whose heart is
he whose name is Coun - sel - or and Power. The pro - tec - tion
of - fered me with - in your ho - ly Word. Help me, Lord, when

kind be-yond all mea-sure gives un - to each day what he deems best—
of his child and trea-sure is a charge that on him-self he laid:
toil and trou-ble meet-ing, e'er to take, as from a fa-ther's hand,

Words: Carolina Sandell Berg (1865); tr. Andrew L. Skoog (1931), P.D.
Music: Oscar Ahnfelt (1872), P.D.

10 9 10 9 D
BLOTT EN DAG

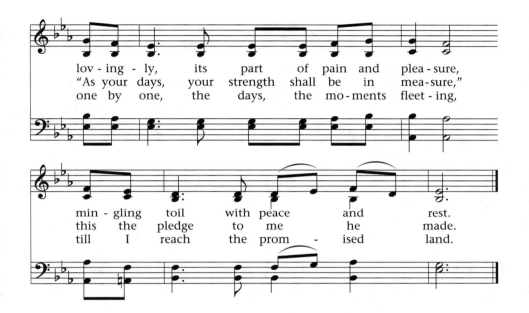

lov - ing - ly,   its   part   of pain and   plea - sure,
"As your days,   your strength shall be in   mea - sure,"
one by one,   the   days,   the mo - ments fleet - ing,

min - gling   toil   with peace   and   rest.
this   the   pledge   to   me   he   made.
till   I   reach   the prom - ised   land.

This is one of "Lina" Sandell's most famous texts. It encourages us to trust in God's providence in all circumstances of life. Ahnfelt, an associate of Lina and of the Swedish evangelist Carl O. Rosenius, wrote the tune for this text, publishing it in one of the later editions of his *Andeliga Sånger*.

146 Onward, Christian Soldiers

1 On - ward, Chris - tian sol - diers, march-ing as to war,
2 Like a might - y ar - my moves the church of God;
3 Crowns and thrones may per - ish, king-doms rise and wane,
4 On - ward, then, O peo - ple, join our hap - py throng:

with the cross of Je - sus go - ing on be - fore.
let us bold - ly fol - low where the saints have trod.
but the church of Je - sus con - stant will re - main;
blend with ours your voic - es in the tri - umph song.

Christ, the roy - al mas - ter, leads a - gainst the foe;
We are not di - vid - ed; all one bod - y we—
gates of hell can nev - er 'gainst that church pre - vail.
Glo - ry, laud, and hon - or un - to Christ the King,

for - ward in - to bat - tle see his ban - ners go!
one in hope and doc - trine, one in char - i - ty.
We have Christ's own prom - ise, and that can - not fail.
we through count - less a - ges with the an - gels sing.

Words: Sabine Baring-Gould (1865), alt., P.D.
Music: Arthur S. Sullivan (1871), P.D.

65 65 D with refrain
ST. GERTRUDE

On - ward, Chris - tian sol - diers, march - ing as to war,

with the cross of Je - sus go - ing on be - fore.

"Onward Christian Soldiers" was written as a processional hymn for children. But its martial imagery, drawn from Ephesians 6:10-18, has often been misinterpreted in our war-obsessed world as triumphalism; consequently some modern hymnals have deleted this text. Sullivan composed the marching tune to fit this text; they were published together in *The Hymnary* (1872), which he edited.

147 Rejoice, O Pure in Heart

1 Re - joice, O pure in heart, re - joice, give thanks, and sing;
2 Bright youth and snow-crowned age, both men and wom - en, raise
3 Still lift your stan - dard high, still chant-ing as you go,

your fes - tal ban - ner wave on high, the cross of Christ your King.
on high your free, ex - ult - ing song, de-clare God's won-drous praise.
from youth to age, by night and day, in glad - ness and in woe.

Refrain

Re-joice, re-joice, re - joice, give thanks, and sing!
re - joice, *re - joice,*

4 At last the march shall end;
the wearied ones shall rest,
the pilgrims reach their home at last,
Jerusalem the blest.
Refrain

5 Praise God, who reigns on high,
the Lord whom we adore:
the Father, Son, and Holy Ghost,
one God forevermore.
Refrain

Words: Edward H. Plumptre (1865), alt., P.D.
Music: Arthur H. Messiter (1883), P.D.

66 86 with refrain
MARION

Plumptre's text was written for processional use in a British choral festival, but its marching metaphor fits equally well for the pilgrimage of the Christian life. Blessed with an appealing melodic contour and a dramatic refrain, Messiter's tune came later, from his days as organist/choirmaster at Trinity Episcopal Church in New York City.

The Church's One Foundation   148

1 The church's one foun-da-tion is Je-sus Christ, her Lord;
2 E - lect from ev-ery na-tion, yet one o'er all the earth;
3 Though with a scorn-ful won-der the world sees her op-pressed,
4 Mid toil and trib-u-la-tion, and tu-mult of her war,

she is his new cre - a - tion by wa-ter and the Word.
her char-ter of sal - va - tion: one Lord, one faith, one birth.
by schisms rent a - sun - der, by her - e - sies dis-tressed,
she waits the con-sum - ma - tion of peace for - ev - er-more,

From heaven he came and sought her to be his ho - ly bride;
One ho - ly name she bless - es, par-takes one ho - ly food,
yet saints their watch are keep - ing; their cry goes up: "How long?"
till with the vi - sion glo - rious her long-ing eyes are blest,

with his own blood he bought her, and for her life he died.
and to one hope she press - es, with ev - ery grace en-dued.
and soon the night of weep - ing shall be the morn of song.
and the great church vic - to - rious shall be the church at rest.

Words: Samuel J. Stone (1866), P.D.
Music: Samuel S. Wesley (1864), P.D.

76 76 D
AURELIA

Stone wrote twelve hymns on the articles of the Apostles' Creed at a time when orthodox Christian beliefs were attacked by various critics. This hymn is his commentary on "the holy catholic church, the communion of saints." This text and Wesley's tune have become inseparable since their first union in the 1868 edition of *Hymns Ancient and Modern.*

149 Immortal, Invisible, God Only Wise

1 Im - mor - tal, in - vis - i - ble, God on - ly wise,
2 Un - rest - ing, un - hast - ing, and si - lent as light,
3 Life - giv - ing Cre - a - tor of both great and small,
4 We wor - ship be - fore you, great Fa - ther of light,

in light in - ac - ces - si - ble hid from our eyes,
nor want - ing nor wast - ing, you rule day and night;
of all life the mak - er, the true life of all;
while an - gels a - dore you, all veil - ing their sight;

most bless - ed, most glo - rious, the An - cient of Days,
your jus - tice like moun - tains high soar - ing a - bove,
we blos - som, then with - er like leaves on the tree,
our prais - es we ren - der, O Fa - ther, to you,

al - might - y, vic - to - rious, your great name we praise.
your clouds which are foun - tains of good - ness and love.
but you are for - ev - er, who was and will be.
whom on - ly the splen - dor of light hides from view.

Words: Walter C. Smith (1867), alt., P.D.
Music: Welsh, in John Roberts' *Caniadau y Cyssegr* (1839), P.D.

11 11 11 11
ST. DENIO

Smith's text catalogues some of the attributes of God, whose works in nature testify to his glory and majesty. An editor of several important Welsh hymnals, "Wild" John Roberts crafted ST. DENIO as a hymn tune from a traditional Welsh ballad.

O Word of God Incarnate   150

1 O Word of God in-car-nate, O Wis-dom from on high,
2 The church from you, dear Mas-ter, re-ceived this gift di-vine;
3 O make your church, dear Sav-ior, a lamp of bur-nished gold

O Truth un-changed, un-chang-ing, O Light of our dark sky:
and still that light is lift-ed o'er all the earth to shine.
to bear be-fore the na-tions your true light as of old.

we praise you for the ra-diance that from the Scrip-ture's page,
It is the chart and com-pass that all life's voy-age through,
O teach your trav-eling pil-grims by this their path to trace

a lan-tern to our foot-steps, shines on from age to age.
mid mists and rocks and quick-sands, still guides, O Christ, to you.
till, clouds and dark-ness end-ed, we see you face to face.

Words: William W. How (1867), alt., P.D.
Music: *Neu-vermehrtes Gesangbuch*, Meiningen (1693); adapt. and harm. Felix Mendelssohn (1847), P.D.

76 76 D
MUNICH

How's text focuses on light: God is light, his Word is a light for our path, and we must be a light to the world.
Appearing in several versions as a Lutheran hymn-tune, MUNICH was harmonized by Mendelssohn in his
oratorio *Elijah* (1846) for the angels' quartet "Cast Thy Burden Upon the Lord."

151 There Were Ninety and Nine

Unison

1 There were nine - ty and nine that safe - ly lay in the
2 "Lord, you have here your nine-ty and nine; are
3 But none of the ran - somed ev - er knew how

shel - ter of the fold. But one was out on the
they not e-nough for you?" "Oh, no," he an - swered,
deep were the wa - ters crossed; nor how dark was the night that

hills a - way, far off from the gates of gold— a -
"This of mine is al - so one of you, and al-
he passed through till he found his sheep that was lost.

way on the moun - tains wild and bare, a - way from the ten - der
though the road be rough and steep, I go to the de - sert to
Out in the de-sert he heard its cry, so sick and help-less and

Words: Elizabeth C. Clephane (1868), alt. Joyce Borger © 2008 Faith Alive Christian Resources
Music: Ira D. Sankey, *Sacred Songs and Solos* (1874); arr. Greg Scheer
© 2008 Faith Alive Christian Resources

irregular
THE NINETY & NINE

shep - herd's care, a - way from the ten - der shep - herd's care.
find my sheep, I go to the de - sert to find my sheep."
read-y to die, so sick and help-less and read-y to die.

4 "Lord, whose is the blood along the way
that marks out the mountain's track?"
"I shed it for one who has gone astray
so that I could bring it back."
"Lord, why are your hands so scarred and torn?"
"My hands were pierced by many a thorn;
my hands were pierced by many a thorn."

5 And all through the mountains, thunder roared
and up from the rocky steep,
a glad cry to the gates of heaven soared:
"Rejoice! I have found my sheep!"
And the angels echoed around the throne,
"Rejoice, for the Lord brings back his own!
Rejoice, for the Lord brings back his own!"

Clephane's text is an extended and imaginative meditation on Jesus' parable of the lost sheep. Sankey, who served
as a musician for Dwight Moody, "spontaneously" composed the melody and often sang it at Moody's crusades.
George B. Shea, a musician associated with the Billy Graham crusades, also sang it often.

152 O Jesus, I Have Promised

1 O Je - sus, I have prom - ised to serve you to the end;
2 O let me feel you near me; the world is ev - er near:
3 O let me hear you speak - ing in ac - cents clear and still,
4 O Je - sus, you have prom - ised to all who fol - low you

be now and ev - er near me, my Mas - ter and my Friend.
I see the sights that daz - zle, the tempt - ing sounds I hear.
a - bove the storms of pas - sion, the mur - murs of self - will.
that where you are in glo - ry your ser - vants shall be too.

I shall not fear the bat - tle if you are by my side,
My foes are ev - er near me, a - round me and with - in;
O speak to re - as - sure me, to has - ten or con - trol;
O guide me, call me, draw me, up - hold me to the end,

nor wan-der from the path - way if you will be my guide.
but, Je - sus, draw still near - er and shield my soul from sin!
and speak to make me lis - ten, O Guard - ian of my soul.
when you in glo - ry take me, my Sav - ior and my Friend.

Words: John E. Bode (1869), alt., P.D.
Music: Finnish (19 c.); harm. David Evans (1927) from the *Revised Church Hymnary* 1927.
Reproduced by permission of Oxford University Press.

76 76 D
NYLAND

Bode wrote this text of consecration for the profession of faith and first communion of his daughter and two sons in 1866. NYLAND (also known as KUORTANE) is a Finnish folk melody that became a hymn-tune in Finland in 1909. Evans harmonized it for inclusion in the *British Church Hymnary* (1927), which he edited. For an alternate harmonization see #250.

The Day You Gave Us, Lord, Is Ended   153

1 The day you gave us, Lord, is end-ed,
2 We thank you that your church, un-sleep-ing
3 As o-ver con-ti-nent and is-land
4 So be it, Lord: your throne shall nev-er,

the dark-ness falls at your be-hest.
while earth rolls on-ward in-to light,
each dawn leads to an-oth-er day,
like earth's proud king-doms, pass a-way.

To you our morn-ing hymns as-cend-ed;
through all the world her watch is keep-ing,
the voice of prayer is nev-er si-lent,
Your king-dom stands and grows for-ev-er,

your praise shall sanc-ti-fy our rest.
and nev-er rests by day or night.
nor do the prais-es die a-way.
un-til there dawns your glo-rious day.

Words: John Ellerton (1870), alt., P.D.
Music: Clement C. Scholefield (1874), P.D.

98 98
ST. CLEMENT

Like the British Empire on which "the sun never set" in Queen Victoria's era, the Christian church is worldwide;
unlike the British Empire (and all other empires) that "pass away," Ellerton helps us confess that Christ's kingdom
is forever. Scholefield's music with its slurred tones was written for this text.

154   At the Name of Jesus

Unison

1 At the name of Je - sus ev - ery knee shall bow,
2 At his voice cre - a - tion sprang at once to sight:
3 Hum-bled for a sea - son, to re - ceive a name
4 bore it up tri - um - phant with its hu - man light,

ev - ery tongue con - fess him King of glo - ry now;
all the an - gel fac - es, all the hosts of light,
from the lips of sin - ners, un - to whom he came;
through all ranks of crea - tures, to the cen - tral height,

'tis the Fa - ther's plea - sure we should call him Lord,
thrones and dom - i - na - tions, stars up - on their way,
faith - ful - ly he bore it spot - less to the last,
to the throne of God - head, to the Fa - ther's breast;

who from the be - gin - ning was the might - y Word.
all the heav-enly or - ders in their great ar - ray.
brought it back vic - to - rious when from death he passed;
filled it with the glo - ry of that per - fect rest.

Words: Caroline M. Noel (1870), alt., P.D.
Music: Ralph Vaughan Williams (1925), P.D.

65 65 D
KING'S WESTON

5 In your hearts enthrone him; there let him subdue
all that is not holy, all that is not true.
Look to him, your Savior, in temptation's hour;
let his will enfold you in its light and power.

6 Christians, this Lord Jesus shall return again,
with his Father's glory, o'er the earth to reign;
for all wreaths of empire meet upon his brow,
and our hearts confess him King of glory now.

Originally written for use in Ascension processionals, Noel's text was inspired in part by the hymnic credo
that Paul quotes in Philippians 2:6-11. Vaughan Williams composed KING'S WESTON for this text, combining
distinctive rhythmic phrases with a soaring melodic climax.

155 Lord, Speak to Me That I May Speak

1 Lord, speak to me that I may speak in liv-ing
2 O lead me, Lord, that I may lead the wan-dering
3 O teach me, Lord, that I may teach the pre-cious
4 O use me, Lord, use e-ven me, just as you

ech-oes of your tone. As you have sought, so
and the wa-vering feet. O feed me, Lord, that
truths which you im-part. And wing my words that
will, and when, and where un-til your bless-ed

let me seek your err-ing chil-dren lost and lone.
I may feed your hun-gry ones with man-na sweet.
they may reach the hid-den depths of man-y a heart.
face I see, your rest, your joy, your glo-ry share.

Words: Frances R. Havergal (1872), alt., P.D.   88 88
Music: Robert A. Schumann (1839), from *Nachstücke,* Op. 23, No. 4, P.D.   CANONBURY

With the heading "A Worker's Prayer," Havergal intended her text to encourage Christian witness in everyday life. In the 19th century, hymnal editors would extract melodies from the great composers to serve as hymn tunes, which is how this melody by Schumann became joined to Havergal's text.

Hosanna, Loud Hosanna 156

1 Ho - san - na, loud ho - san - na the lit - tle chil - dren sang;
2 From Ol - i - vet they fol - lowed 'mid an ex - ul - tant crowd,
3 "Ho - san - na in the high - est!" That an - cient song we sing,

through pil - lared court and tem - ple the love - ly an - them rang.
the vic - tory palm branch wav - ing, and chant - ing clear and loud.
for Christ is our Re - deem - er, the Lord of heaven, our King.

To Je - sus, who had blessed them, close fold - ed to his breast,
The Lord of earth and heav - en rode on in low - ly state,
O may we ev - er praise him with heart and life and voice,

the chil - dren sang their prais - es, the sim - plest and the best.
nor scorned that lit - tle chil - dren should on his bid - ding wait.
and in his bliss - ful pres - ence e - ter - nal - ly re - joice.

Words: Jennette Threlfall (1873), P.D.
Music: *Gesangbuch der Herzogl,* Würtemburg (1784), P.D.

76 76 D
ELLACOMBE

In this Palm Sunday text, Threlfall helps us experience Christ's triumphal entry into Jerusalem through the role of the children in that event. For the tune, see "Fill Thou My Life, O Lord, My God" (142).

157 Like a River Glorious

1 Like a riv-er glo-rious is God's per-fect peace, o-ver
2 Hid-den in the hol-low of his might-y hand, where no

all vic-to-rious in its bright in-crease: per-fect, yet still
harm can fol-low, in his strength we stand. We may trust him

flow-ing full-er ev-ery day; per-fect, yet still grow-ing
ful-ly all for us to do; those who trust him whol-ly

Refrain

deep-er all the way. Trust-ing in the Fa-ther, hearts are ful-ly
find him whol-ly true.

blest, find-ing, as he prom-ised, per-fect peace and rest.

Words: Frances R. Havergal (1878), alt., P.D.
Music: James Mountain (1876), P.D.

65 65 D with refrain
WYE VALLEY

Like the psalms of trust in the Old Testament, this text helps us affirm that trusting in God produces "perfect peace and rest." The serene tune, with its melodic repetitions, was composed by Mountain for Havergal's text and published in their *Hymns of Consecration and Faith* (1876).

Take My Life and Let It Be 158

1 Take my life and let it be con-se-crat-ed,
2 Take my hands and let them move at the im-pulse
3 Take my voice and let me sing al-ways, on-ly,
4 Take my sil-ver and my gold; not a mite would

Lord, to thee. Take my mo-ments and my days; let them
of thy love. Take my feet and let them be swift and
for my King. Take my lips and let them be filled with
I with-hold. Take my in-tel-lect and use ev-ery

flow in end-less praise, let them flow in end-less praise.
beau-ti-ful for thee, swift and beau-ti-ful for thee.
mes-sag-es from thee, filled with mes-sag-es from thee.
power as thou shalt choose, ev-ery power as thou shalt choose.

5 Take my will and make it thine;
it shall be no longer mine.
Take my heart—it is thine own;
it shall be thy royal throne,
it shall be thy royal throne.

6 Take my love; my Lord, I pour
at thy feet its treasure store.
Take myself, and I will be
ever, only, all for thee,
ever, only, all for thee.

Words: Frances R. Havergal (1874), P.D.
Music: Henri A. Cesar Malan (1827), P.D.

77 77 with repeat
HENDON

A "Self-Consecration to Christ," Havergal's text is a catalogue hymn that lists the most important parts of our lives as symbols of everything that we are to dedicate to the Lord's service. Lowell Mason brought HENDON from France to the United States. Eventually text and music were united; however, the long opening lines in most stanzas are not well supported by this tune of shorter phrases.

159 O the Deep, Deep Love of Jesus

1 O the deep, deep love of Je-sus, vast, un-mea-sured, bound-less, free!
2 O the deep, deep love of Je-sus—spread his praise from shore to shore!
3 O the deep, deep love of Je-sus, love of ev-ery love the best!

Roll-ing as a might-y o-cean in its full-ness o-ver me!
How he loves us, ev-er loves us, chang-es nev-er, nev-er-more!
'Tis an o-cean vast of bless-ing, 'tis a ha-ven sweet of rest!

Un-der-neath me, all a-round me, is the cur-rent of thy love—
How he watch-es o'er his loved ones, died to call them all his own;
O the deep, deep love of Je-sus— 'tis a heaven of heavens to me;

lead-ing on-ward, lead-ing home-ward, to thy glo-rious rest a-bove!
how for them he's in-ter-ced-ing, watch-ing o'er them from the throne!
and it lifts me up to glo-ry, for it lifts me up to thee!

Words: Samuel Trevor Francis (c. 1890), alt., P.D.
Music: Thomas J. Williams (1890), P.D.

87 87 D
EBENEZER

A member of the Plymouth Brethren, Francis combines ocean and water imagery to marvel at the great love of Jesus for his people. Suitably joined to this cosmic text is the Welsh tune EBENEZER, given here in E minor; for "Thy Strong Word" (#220) it is set in F minor.

Breathe on Me, Breath of God   160

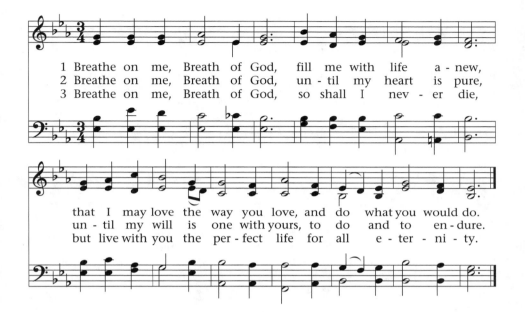

1 Breathe on me, Breath of God, fill me with life a - new,
2 Breathe on me, Breath of God, un - til my heart is pure,
3 Breathe on me, Breath of God, so shall I nev - er die,

that I may love the way you love, and do what you would do.
un - til my will is one with yours, to do and to en - dure.
but live with you the per - fect life for all e - ter - ni - ty.

Words: Edwin Hatch (1878), alt., P.D.   66 86
Music: Robert Jackson (1878), P.D.   TRENTHAM

Originally written as a hymn for ordination, this is a sung prayer for renewal by the Holy Spirit—a "mini"
pneumatology (doctrine of the Holy Spirit). Unfortunately, the mannerist Victorian hymn melody by Jackson
traditionally associated with this text is hardly adequate for this prayer's fervor.

161 Thine Is the Glory

1 Thine is the glo - ry, ris - en, con - quering Son;
2 Lo, Je - sus meets thee, ris - en from the tomb!
3 No more we doubt thee, glo - rious Prince of life;

end - less is the vic - tory thou o'er death hast won!
Lov - ing - ly he greets thee, scat - ters fear and gloom;
life is naught with - out thee; aid us in our strife;

An - gels in bright rai - ment rolled the stone a - way,
let his church with glad - ness, hymns of tri - umph sing,
make us more than con - querors, through thy death - less love;

kept the fold - ed grave - clothes where thy bod - y lay.
for the Lord now live - th; death hath lost its sting!
bring us safe through Jor - dan to thy home a - bove.

Words: Edmond Budry (1904); tr. R. Birch Hoyle (1923), P.D.
Music: George Frideric Handel (1748), P.D.

55 65 65 65 with refrain
JUDAS MACCABAEUS

Thine is the glo - ry, ris - en con - quering Son;

end - less is the vic - tory thou o'er death hast won!

Written in French by a Swiss pastor, this Easter text was likely inspired by an Advent hymn of Friederich-Heinrich Ranke (1798-1876) which used this tune by Handel. This music first appeared in Handel's oratorio *Joshua* and was transferred by him to his oratorio *Judas Maccabeus* from 1751 onward for the chorus "See, the Conquering Hero Comes." It was used as the melody for Wesley's "Christ the Lord Is Risen Today" in Thomas Butts' *Harmonia Sacra* (1760).

162 Lift High the Cross

Refrain Unison

Lift high the cross, the love of Christ pro - claim till
all the world a - dore his sa - cred name.

Harmony

1 Come, Chris - tians, fol - low where our Sav - ior led, our
2 All new - born ser - vants of the Cru - ci - fied bear
3 From north and south, from east and west we raise in
4 O Lord, once lift - ed on the tree of pain, draw

To Refrain

King vic - to - rious, Je - sus Christ, our Head.
on their brows the seal of him who died.
grow - ing un - i - son our song of praise.
all the world to seek you once a - gain.

5 Let every race and
every language tell of
him who saves our
lives from death and hell.
Refrain

6 Set up your throne,
that earth's despair
may cease beneath
the shadow of its
healing peace. *Refrain*

7 So shall our song
of triumph ever be:
praise to the Crucified
for victory!
Refrain

Words: George W. Kitchin and Michael R. Newbolt
Music: Sydney H. Nicholson
Words and Music © 1974 Hope Publishing Company

10 10 with refrain
CRUCIFER

Though this processional text initially appears to focus on the cross of Christ, it is really a missional hymn that calls us to spread the gospel of Christ's kingdom throughout the world. Newbolt's revision of Kitchin's original text and Nicholson's glorious tune were published in the 1916 Supplement to *Hymns Ancient and Modern.*

This Joyful Eastertide 163

1 This joy-ful Eas-ter-tide, a-way with sin and sad -
Our Lord, the cru-ci-fied, has filled our hearts with glad -
2 My be-ing shall re-joice se-cure with-in God's keep -
un-til the trum-pet voice shall wake us from our sleep -
3 Death's wa-ters lost their chill when Je-sus crossed the riv -
His love shall reach me still; his mer-cy is for-ev -

Refrain

(1) - ness!
 - ness.
(2) - ing,
 - ing.   Had Christ, who once was slain, not burst his three-day pris -
(3) - er.
 - er.

on, our faith would be in vain. But now has Christ a-ris-en, a-

ris-en, a-ris-en, but now has Christ a-ris-en.

Words: George R. Woodward (1894), alt., P.D.
Music: Joachim Oudaen's *David's Psalmen* (1685); harm. Dale Grotenhuis (1984)
© 1987 Faith Alive Christian Resources

67 67 with refrain
VREUCHTEN

Woodward wrote the "joyful" text of this Easter carol to fit the Dutch tune, which was originally associated with a love song. This music is distinguished by the melismas (multiple tones on one text syllable) in the stanzas and the most fitting rising sequences on "arisen" in the refrain.

164 Let Us Break Bread Together

1 Let us break bread to-geth-er on our knees;
2 Let us drink wine to-geth-er on our knees;
3 Let us praise God to-geth-er on our knees;

let us break bread to-geth-er on our knees.
let us drink wine to-geth-er on our knees.
let us praise God to-geth-er on our knees.

Refrain

When I fall on my knees, with my face to the Lord of life,

O Lord, have mer-cy on me.

Words and Music: Afro-Amerian spiritual (18th c.); harm. Dale Grotenhuis   73 73 with refrain
(1984) © 1987 Faith Alive Christian Resources   BREAK BREAD TOGETHER

There are variants of this oral-tradition text as well as alterations in modern hymnals; the post-Civil War version
provided here turned a song used by black slaves to convene secret meetings into a eucharistic hymn. The
popularity of this choral mini-gem grew after publication in *The Second Book of Negro Spirituals* (1926) compiled
by the brothers James W. and J. Rosamond Johnson.

Lord, I Want to Be a Christian 165

1 Lord, I want to be a Chris-tian in my heart, in my heart.
2 Lord, I want to be more lov-ing in my heart, in my heart.
3 Lord, I want to be more ho-ly in my heart, in my heart.
4 Lord, I want to be like Je - sus in my heart, in my heart.

Lord, I want to be a Chris-tian in my heart.
Lord, I want to be more lov-ing in my heart.
Lord, I want to be more ho-ly in my heart.
Lord, I want to be like Je - sus in my heart.

In my heart, in my heart,
in my heart, in my heart,

Lord, I want to be a Chris-tian in my heart.
Lord, I want to be more lov-ing in my heart.
Lord, I want to be more ho-ly in my heart.
Lord, I want to be like Je - sus in my heart.

Words and Music: Afro-American spiritual (18th c.), P.D.

11 11 11 with repeats
LORD, I WANT TO BE A CHRISTIAN

This is a prayer not only to become a Christian but also to live like one in a loving, holy, and intimate walk with Jesus. Text and music were first published in *Folk Songs of the American Negro* (1907), compiled by the brothers Frederick J. and John W. Work.

166 When Jesus Wept

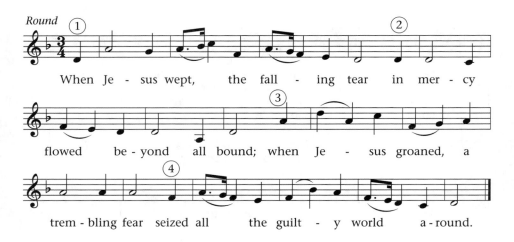

Words and Music: William Billings, *The New England Psalm Singer* (1770), P.D.

irregular
WHEN JESUS WEPT

A tanner by trade and an amateur musician, Billings is best known for his fuguing tunes and anthems that were published in a great assortment of Northern-U.S. tunebooks and Southern-U.S. shape-note hymnals. "When Jesus Wept" is a round in the rugged style so typical of Billings.

There Is a Balm in Gilead   167

Refrain

There is a balm in Gil-e-ad to make the wound-ed whole,

Fine

there is a balm in Gil-e-ad to heal the sin-sick soul.

1 Some-times I feel dis-cour-aged and think my work's in vain,
2 If you can-not preach like Pe-ter, if you can-not pray like Paul,

To Refrain

but then the Ho-ly Spir-it re-vives my soul a-gain.
you can tell the love of Je-sus and say, "He died for all."

Words and Music: Afro-American spiritual (19th c.), P.D.

irregular
BALM IN GILEAD

It is thought that this spiritual developed in camp meetings in the early nineteenth century. The text draws on the image of Gilead, which in biblical times was a source of spices and medical ointments. The refrain turns Jeremiah's rhetorical question (Jer. 8:22) into a testimony that Christ is the balm for the "sin-sick soul."

168 Were You There

1 Were you there when they cru - ci - fied my Lord? Were you
2 Were you there when they nailed him to the tree? Were you
3 Were you there when they laid him in the tomb? Were you
4 Were you there when God raised him from the tomb? Were you

there when they cru - ci - fied my Lord? Oh,
there when they nailed him to the tree? Oh,
there when they laid him in the tomb? Oh,
there when God raised him from the tomb? Oh,

some - times it caus - es me to trem - ble, trem - ble, trem - ble.
some - times it caus - es me to trem - ble, trem - ble, trem - ble.
some - times it caus - es me to trem - ble, trem - ble, trem - ble.
some - times it caus - es me to trem - ble, trem - ble, trem - ble.

Were you there when they cru - ci - fied my Lord?
Were you there when they nailed him to the tree?
Were you there when they laid him in the tomb?
Were you there when God raised him from the tomb?

Words and Music: Afro-American spiritual (19th c.); harm. C. Winfred Douglas (1940), P.D.

10 10 14 10
WERE YOU THERE

This beloved spiritual probably predates the Civil War but was published much later in William Barton's *Old Plantation Hymns* (1899). The span of time is collapsed as we become witnesses to Christ's crucifixion and death; the resurrection stanza is a later addition. Note the moaning effect of the "Oh" and the syncopations on "tremble."

When Israel Was in Egypt's Land   169

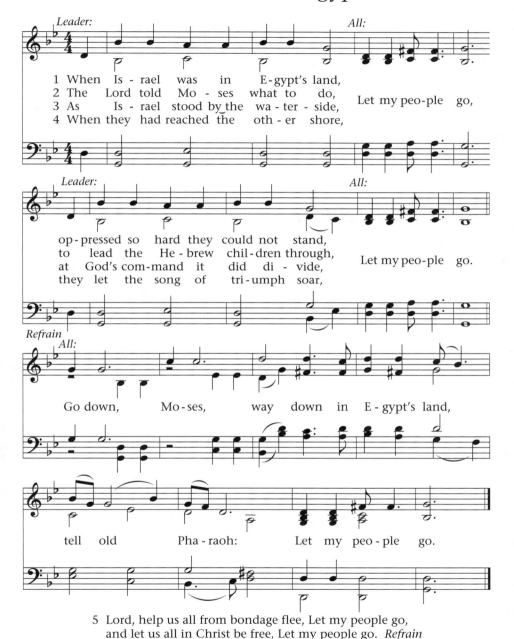

1 When Is - rael was in E - gypt's land,
2 The Lord told Mo - ses what to do,   Let my peo-ple go,
3 As Is - rael stood by the wa - ter - side,
4 When they had reached the oth - er shore,

op - pressed so hard they could not stand,
to lead the He - brew chil - dren through,   Let my peo - ple go.
at God's com-mand it did di - vide,
they let the song of tri - umph soar,

Refrain

Go down, Mo - ses, way down in E - gypt's land,

tell old Pha - raoh: Let my peo - ple go.

5 Lord, help us all from bondage flee, Let my people go,
and let us all in Christ be free, Let my people go. *Refrain*

Words and Music: Afro-American spiritual)19th c.); harm. John W. Work (1896), P.D.   86 85 with refrain
GO DOWN, MOSES

First published in *Jubilee Songs* (1872), made popular by the Jubilee Singers of Fisk University, this African-American spiritual dates from the slavery era prior to the Civil War in the United States. It is performed in call-and-response form, and over time acquired some 24 stanzas. The response phrase boldly calls for freedom from all types of oppression—ultimately, as in stanza 5, a freedom found in Christ.

170   I Love Your Church, O Lord

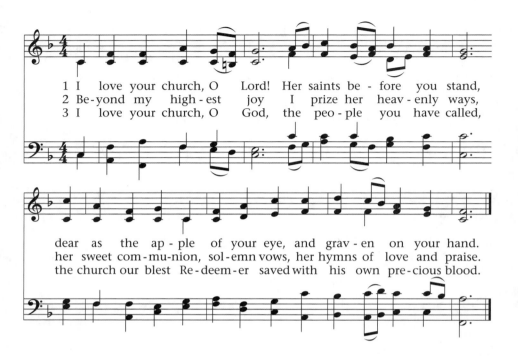

1 I love your church, O Lord! Her saints be-fore you stand,
2 Be-yond my high-est joy I prize her heav-enly ways,
3 I love your church, O God, the peo-ple you have called,

dear as the ap-ple of your eye, and grav-en on your hand.
her sweet com-mu-nion, sol-emn vows, her hymns of love and praise.
the church our blest Re-deem-er saved with his own pre-cious blood.

Words: Timothy Dwight (1800), alt., P.D.
Music: Aaron Williams (1770), P.D.

66 86
ST. THOMAS

After the American Revolution, Yale University president Timothy Dwight revised the texts of Isaac Watts to remove British references. He also added some hymns of his own (including this one, which originally and erroneously treated the Christian church and the kingdom of Christ as one entity) in the publication known as *Dwight's Watts*. ST. THOMAS is a joyful tune extracted from a longer melody by Williams.

What Wondrous Love   171

1 What won-drous love is this, O my soul, O my soul! What
2 When I was sink-ing down, sink-ing down, sink-ing down, when
3 To God and to the Lamb I will sing, I will sing, to
4 And when from death I'm free, I'll sing on, I'll sing on, and

won-drous love is this, O my soul! What won-drous love is
I was sink-ing down, sink-ing down; when I was sink-ing
God and to the Lamb I will sing; to God and to the
when from death I'm free, I'll sing on; and when from death I'm

this that caused the Lord of bliss to bear the dread-ful curse
down be-neath God's right-eous frown, Christ laid a-side his crown
Lamb, who is the great I AM— while mil-lions join the theme,
free, I'll sing and joy-ful be, and through e-ter-ni-ty

for my soul, for my soul, to bear the dread-ful curse for my soul?
for my soul, for my soul, Christ laid a-side his crown for my soul.
I will sing, I will sing, while mil-lions join the theme, I will sing.
I'll sing on, I'll sing on, and through e-ter-ni-ty I'll sing on.

Words: Stith Mead's *A General Selection* (1811), P.D.
Music: William Walker's *Southern Harmony* (1835); harm. Emily R. Brink, 1986
© 1987 Faith Alive Christian Resources

12 9 12 12 9
WONDROUS LOVE

This text, a meditation on Christ's "wondrous love," appeared anonymously in separate Baptist and Methodist collections in 1811. A generation later the text was published with the pentatonic WONDROUS LOVE tune in *Southern Harmony* and in *The Sacred Harp*, both of which are classic volumes of shape-note hymnody in the United States.

172 Brethren, We Have Met to Worship

1 Breth-ren, we have met to wor-ship and a-dore the Lord our God;
2 Sis-ters, will you join and help us? Mo-ses' sis-ter aid-ed him;
3 Let us pause be-fore our Mak-er and in si-lence hear his voice;
4 Let us love our God su-preme-ly, let us love each oth-er too;

will you pray with all your pow-er, while we try to preach the word?
will you help the trem-bling mour-ners who are strug-gling hard with sin?
Christ the Liv-ing Word now meets us; in his truth let us re-joice.
let us love and pray for sin-ners till our God makes all things new.

All is vain, un-less the Spir-it of the Ho-ly One comes down:
Tell them all a-bout the Sav-ior— tell them that he will be found:
What we are should not ap-pall us for his mer-cy meets us here;
Then he'll call us home to heav-en, at his ta-ble we'll sit down;

Breth-ren, pray, and ho-ly man-na will be show-ered all a-round.
Sis-ters, pray, and ho-ly man-na will be show-ered all a-round.
we are now made one in Je-sus, may our wor-ship be sin-cere.
Christ will gird him-self and serve us with sweet man-na all a-round.

Words: Attr. To George Atkins (1819), sts. 1,2,4; st. 3, Bryan Jeffery Leech   87 87 D
© 1990 Hope Publishing Company
Music: attr. William Moore, *Columbian Harmony* (1825), P.D.   HOLY MANNA

Originally a camp meeting song, this text is rich with biblical and evangelical imagery about conversion, revival, preaching, and prayer. Text and tune were united in Moore's *Columbian Harmony*. Given the pentatonic shape of this melody, try singing it as a round, at one-measure entries.

My Faith Looks Up to Thee 173

1 My faith looks up to thee, thou Lamb of Cal - va - ry,
2 May thy rich grace im-part strength to my faint - ing heart,
3 While life's dark maze I tread and griefs a - round me spread,
4 When life's swift race is run, death's cold work al - most done,

Sav - ior di - vine! Now hear me while I pray, take all my
my zeal in - spire. As thou hast died for me, O may my
be thou my guide. Bid dark-ness turn to day, wipe sor-row's
be near to me. Blest Sav - ior, then in love fear and dis -

guilt a - way. O let me from this day be whol - ly thine!
love to thee, pure, warm, and change-less be, a liv - ing fire!
tears a - way, nor let me ev - er stray from thee a - side.
trust re-move. O bear me safe a - bove, re-deemed and free!

Words: Ray Palmer (1830), alt., P.D.
Music: Lowell Mason (1832), P.D.

664 6664
OLIVET

Inspired by a German poem in which a sinner kneels at the cross of Christ, Palmer wrote these comforting words during a time of illness and loneliness. Mason, who composed the tune specifically for this text, foretold that Palmer "will be best known to posterity as the author of this text."

174 What a Friend We Have in Jesus

1 What a friend we have in Je - sus, all our sins and griefs to bear!
2 Have we tri - als and temp-ta-tions? Is there trou-ble an - y-where?
3 Are we weak and heav - y la - den, cum-bered with a load of care?

What a priv - i - lege to car - ry ev - ery-thing to God in prayer!
We should nev - er be dis - cour - aged—take it to the Lord in prayer.
Pre - cious Sav-ior, still our ref - uge— take it to the Lord in prayer.

Oh, what peace we of - ten for - feit, oh, what need-less pain we bear—
Can we find a friend so faith-ful who will all our sor-rows share?
Do your friends de - spise, for-sake you? Take it to the Lord in prayer.

all be - cause we do not car - ry ev - ery-thing to God in prayer.
Je - sus knows our ev - ery weak-ness— take it to the Lord in prayer.
In his arms he'll take and shield you; you will find a sol-ace there.

Words: Joseph M. Scriven (1855), P.D.
Music: Charles C. Converse (1868); setting *The Hymn Book* (1971), P.D.

87 87 D
CONVERSE

A member of the Plymouth Brethren, Scriven wrote these words to comfort his mother (and no doubt himself) following the death of his second fiancee; his first had died some years earlier. Converse composed the music for these words; the union of text and tune were cemented in *Gospel Hymns and Sacred Songs* (1875) compiled by Philip Bliss and Ira Sankey.

Jesus Loves Me, This I Know   175

1 Je - sus loves me! This I know, for the Bi - ble tells me so.
2 Je - sus loves me— he who died heav-en's gate to o - pen wide.
3 Je - sus loves me, this I know, as he loved so long a - go,

Lit - tle ones to him be-long; they are weak, but he is strong.
He will wash a - way my sin, let his lit - tle child come in.
tak - ing chil-dren on his knee, say - ing, "Let them come to me."

Refrain

Yes, Je - sus loves me! Yes, Je - sus loves me!

Yes, Je - sus loves me! The Bi - ble tells me so.

Words: st. 1-2, Anna B. Warner (1859); st. 3, David R. McGuire (1971), P.D.
Music: William B. Bradbury (1861), P.D.

77 77 with refrain
JESUS LOVES ME

This famous hymn for children of God of all ages, altered in various modern hymnals, is extracted from a forgotten moralistic novel by Warner and her sister Susan. Both women taught Sunday school and Bible classes for West Point cadets. Bradbury provided the refrain line and the music in his popular Sunday school songbook, *The Golden Shower* (1862).

176   He Leadeth Me

Words: Joseph H. Gilmore (1862), P.D.
Music: William B. Bradbury (1864), P.D.

88 88 with refrain
AUGHTON

3 Lord, I would clasp thy hand in mine,
  nor ever murmur nor repine;
  content, whatever lot I see,
  since 'tis my God that leadeth me.

4 And when my task on earth is done,
  when, by thy grace, the victory's won,
  e'en death's cold wave I will not flee,
  since God through Jordan leadeth me.

Gilmore's text was inspired by his preaching on Psalm 23. Bradbury provided the music and the refrain line. This gospel hymn is one of the finest examples of Christian singing about the comfort of trusting in God's providence.

177   My Jesus, I Love Thee

1 My Je - sus, I love thee, I know thou art mine;
2 I love thee be - cause thou hast first lov - ed me
3 I'll love thee in life, I will love thee in death,
4 In man - sions of glo - ry and end - less de - light,

for thee all the fol - lies of sin I re - sign;
and pur - chased my par - don on Cal - va - ry's tree;
and praise thee as long as thou lend - est me breath,
I'll ev - er a - dore thee in heav - en so bright;

my gra - cious Re - deem - er, my Sav - ior art thou;
I love thee for wear - ing the thorns on thy brow;
and say when the death - dew lies cold on my brow:
I'll sing with the glit - ter - ing crown on my brow:

if ev - er I loved thee, my Je - sus 'tis now.
if ev - er I loved thee, my Je - sus 'tis now.
If ev - er I loved thee, my Je - sus 'tis now.
If ev - er I loved thee, my Je - sus 'tis now.

Words: William R. Featherstone (c. 1862), P.D.
Music: Adoniram J. Gordon (1876), P.D.

11 11 11 11
GORDON

Featherstone is a virtually unknown Canadian from Montreal. His text, now a beloved hymn of devotion to Jesus, appeared anonymously in *The London Hymn Book* (1864), where Gordon, a Baptist preacher, saw it and composed the present tune for it in 1872. Text and tune were published together in *The Service of Song for Baptist Churches* (1876) for which Gordon was one of the editors.

Holy Spirit, Truth Divine   178

1 Ho - ly Spir - it, truth di - vine, dawn up - on this soul of mine.
2 Ho - ly Spir - it, love di - vine, glow with - in this heart of mine.
3 Ho - ly Spir - it, power di - vine, fill and nerve this will of mine.
4 Ho - ly Spir - it, law di - vine, reign with - in this soul of mine.

Voice of God and in - ward light, wake my spir - it, clear my sight.
Kin - dle ev - ery high de - sire, pu - ri - fy me with your fire.
Bold - ly may I al - ways live, brave - ly serve, and glad - ly give.
Be my law, and I shall be firm - ly bound, for - ev - er free.

5 Holy Spirit, peace divine,
   still this restless heart of mine.
   Speak to calm this tossing sea,
   grant me your tranquility.

6 Holy Spirit, joy divine,
   gladden now this heart of mine.
   In the desert ways I sing—
   spring, O Living Water, spring!

Words: Samuel Longfellow (1864), alt., P.D.
Music: Orlando Gibbons (1623), P.D.

77 77
SONG 13

This catalogue hymn helps us pray for various ministries of the Holy Spirit. It was written by a Unitarian preacher and published in the Unitarian hymnal *Hymns of the Spirit* (1864). Gibbons' tune was composed originally for a paraphrase drawn from the Song of Songs, but since its inclusion in *Hymns Ancient and Modern* (1861) it has served a variety of hymn texts.

179 Shall We Gather at the River

1 Shall we gath - er at the riv-er, where bright an - gel feet have trod,
2 On the mar-gin of the riv-er, wash - ing up its sil - ver spray,
3 Ere we reach the shin-ing riv-er, lay we ev - ery bur-den down;
4 Soon we'll reach the sil - ver riv-er, soon our pil-grim-age will cease;

with its crys - tal tide for - ev - er flow-ing by the throne of God?
we will walk and wor - ship ev - er, all the hap-py gold-en day.
grace our spir - its will de - liv - er, and pro-vide a robe and crown.
soon our hap - py hearts will quiv - er with the mel - o - dy of peace.

Refrain

Yes, we'll gath-er at the riv - er, the beau-ti-ful, the beau-ti-ful riv-er;

gath - er with the saints at the riv-er that flows by the throne of God.

Words and Music: Robert Lowry (1864), P.D.

87 87 with refrain
HANSON PLACE

Written during an outbreak of an infectious disease in New York City in 1864, Lowry's words drew people's attention from death to the crystal river of life (Rev. 22:1). He provided the music as well, calling it a "brass band march"; the hymn was published in *Happy Voices* (1865), a hymnal edited by Lowry and William Doane.

O Little Town of Bethlehem 180

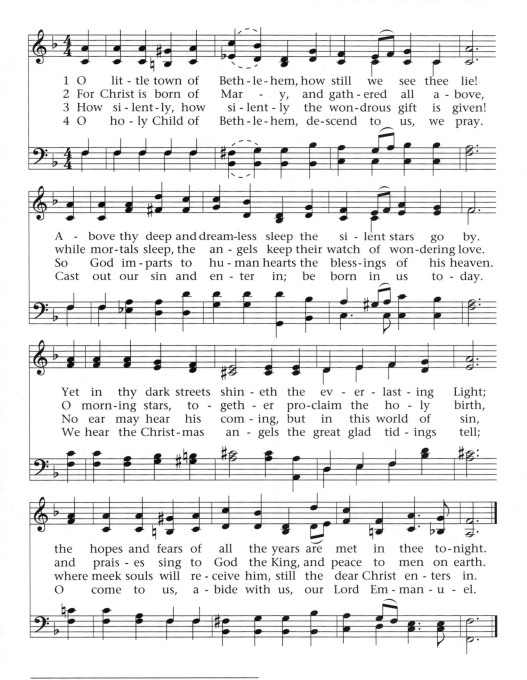

1 O lit - tle town of Beth - le - hem, how still we see thee lie!
2 For Christ is born of Mar - y, and gath - ered all a - bove,
3 How si - lent - ly, how si - lent - ly the won - drous gift is given!
4 O ho - ly Child of Beth - le - hem, de - scend to us, we pray.

A - bove thy deep and dream-less sleep the si - lent stars go by.
while mor - tals sleep, the an - gels keep their watch of won - dering love.
So God im - parts to hu - man hearts the bless - ings of his heaven.
Cast out our sin and en - ter in; be born in us to - day.

Yet in thy dark streets shin - eth the ev - er - last - ing Light;
O morn - ing stars, to - geth - er pro - claim the ho - ly birth,
No ear may hear his com - ing, but in this world of sin,
We hear the Christ - mas an - gels the great glad tid - ings tell;

the hopes and fears of all the years are met in thee to - night.
and prais - es sing to God the King, and peace to men on earth.
where meek souls will re - ceive him, still the dear Christ en - ters in.
O come to us, a - bide with us, our Lord Em - man - u - el.

Words: Phillips Brooks (1868), P.D.
Music: Lewis H. Redner (1868), P.D.

86 86 76 86
ST. LOUIS

Inspired by his trip to Bethlehem a few years earlier, Brooks wrote this Christmas text for a Sunday school celebration in collaboration with his organist, Redner, who composed the music "in great haste." The text moves from nostalgia for Bethlehem to a prayer for Christ "to be born in us today."

181 We Have Heard the Joyful Sound

1 We have heard the joy-ful sound: Je-sus saves! Je-sus saves!
2 Waft it on the roll-ing tide: Je-sus saves! Je-sus saves!

Spread the ti-dings all a-round: Je-sus saves! Je-sus saves!
Tell to sin-ners far and wide: Je-sus saves! Je-sus saves!

Bear the news to ev-ery land, climb the steeps and cross the waves.
Sing, ye is-lands of the sea! Ech-o back, ye o-cean caves!

On-ward! 'tis our Lord's com-mand; Je-sus saves! Je-sus saves!
Earth shall keep her ju-bi-lee: Je-sus saves! Je-sus saves!

3 Sing above the battle strife:
   Jesus saves! Jesus saves!
By his death and endless life,
   Jesus saves! Jesus saves!
Sing it softly through the gloom,
   when the heart for mercy craves;
sing in triumph o'er the tomb:
   Jesus saves! Jesus saves!

4 Give the winds a mighty voice:
   Jesus saves! Jesus saves!
Let the nations now rejoice—
   Jesus saves! Jesus saves!
Shout salvation full and free,
   highest hills and deepest caves;
this our song of victory:
   Jesus saves! Jesus saves!

Words: Priscilla J. Owens (1868), P.D.
Music: William J. Kirkpatrick (1882), P.D.

76 76 77 76
JESUS SAVES

Like Psalm 96, this text celebrates God's saving acts. Owens wrote the words for a missionary service in her Sunday school and sang them to "Vive le Roi" from Meyerbeer's opera *Les Huguenots*. Gospel hymn composer and editor Kirkpatrick composed the tune now associated with this evangelical text.

My Life Flows On in Endless Song/ 182
How Can I Keep from Singing?

1 My life flows on in end-less song; a-bove earth's lam-en-ta-tion,
2 Through all the tu-mult and the strife, I hear that mu-sic ring-ing.

I catch the sweet, though far-off hymn that hails a new cre-a-tion.
It finds an ech-o in my soul. How can I keep from sing-ing?

Refrain

No storm can shake my in-most calm while to that Rock I'm cling-ing.

Since Christ is Lord of heav-en and earth, how can I keep from sing-ing?

3 What though my joys
   and comforts die?
  The Lord my Savior liveth.
  What though the darkness
   gather round?
  Songs in the night he giveth.

4 The peace of Christ
   makes fresh my heart,
  a fountain ever springing!
  All things are mine
   since I am his!
  How can I keep from singing?

Words and Music: attr. to Robert Lowry (1860), alt., P.D.

87 87 with refrain
ENDLESS SONG

The "song" of this text becomes an extended metaphor for an intimate walk with Jesus who gives us peace in all circumstances of life. Though attributed to Lowry and published in his *Bright Jewels for the Sunday School* (1869), a version of these words appeared earlier, and some scholars think the roots of this hymn lie among the Quakers.

183 Dear Father of All Humankind

Unison

1 Dear Fa - ther of all hu - man-kind, for-
give our fool - ish ways! Re - clothe us in our
right - ful mind, in pur - er lives your serv - ice find, in
deep - er rev - erence, praise, in deep - er rev - erence, praise.

2 In sim - ple trust like theirs who heard, be-
side the Syr - ian Sea, the gra - cious call - ing
of the Lord, let us, like them, o - bey his word, "Rise
up and fol - low me. Rise up and fol - low me."

3 O sab - bath rest by Gal - i - lee! O
calm of hills a - bove, where Je - sus knelt to
share with thee the sil - ence of e - ter - ni - ty, in-
ter - pret - ed by love, in - ter - pret - ed by love!

Words: John G. Whittier (1872), P.D.
Music: C. Hubert H. Parry (1888), P.D.

86 88 66
REPTON

4 Drop your still dews of quietness
   till all our strivings cease;
   take from our souls the strain and stress
   and let our ordered lives confess
   the beauty of your peace,
   the beauty of your peace.

5 Breathe through the heat of our desires
   your coolness and your balm;
   let sense be dumb, let flesh retire,
   speak through the earthquake, wind, and fire,
   O still, small voice of calm,
   O still, small voice of calm.

This meditative text by the Quaker poet Whittier combines "the beauty of peace" with a call for "purer lives." The original first line, which reads, "Dear Lord and Father of mankind," is variously altered in modern hymnals. The tune is from *Judith,* an oratorio by Parry; Frederick Maker's REST (1887) is also used for this text.

184 Go, Tell It on the Mountain

Refrain Unison

Go,   tell it on the moun-tain,   o-ver the hills and   ev-ery-where;

go,   tell it on the moun-tain that   Je-sus Christ is   born.

1 While shep-herds kept their watch-ing o'er si-lent flocks by   night,
2 The   shep-herds feared and trem-bled when lo!   a-bove the   earth
3 Down in   a   low-ly   sta-ble   the hum-ble Christ was   born,

Repeat refrain

be-hold, through-out the heav-ens there shone a   ho-ly   light.
rang out   the   an-gel cho-rus   that hailed our Sav-ior's   birth.
and God   sent   us sal-va-tion that bless-ed Christ-mas   morn.

Words and Music: Afro-American spiritual (19th c.), P.D.

76 76 with refrain
GO TELL IT

This Christmas spiritual was popularized by the Fisk University Jubilee Singers in their choral concerts in the late nineteenth century. Since it comes from oral tradition, it is not surprising to find variants of the text (even an Easter version!) and the tune in various sources.

Blessed Assurance: Jesus Is Mine   185

1 Bless-ed as-sur-ance: Je-sus is mine! Oh, what a fore-taste of
2 Joy-ful con-fes-sion: I am his own! Fol-low-ing Je-sus, I'm
3 Per-fect sub-mis-sion: all is at rest, I in my Sav-ior am

glo-ry di-vine! Heir of sal-va-tion, pur-chase of
nev-er a-lone. Born of his Spir-it, I am re-
hap-py and blest; watch-ing and wait-ing, look-ing a-

God, born of his Spir-it, washed in his blood.
stored, chal-lenged to serve my Sav-ior and Lord.
bove, filled with his good-ness, kept in his love.

Refrain

This is my sto-ry, this is my song, prais-ing my Sav-ior all the day long;

this is my sto-ry, this is my song, prais-ing my Sav-ior all the day long.

Words: st. 1, 3, Fanny J. Crosby (1873); st. 2, Marie J. Post (1985) © 1987 Faith Alive   9 10 9 9 with refrain
    Christian Resources
Music: Phoebe P. Knapp (1873), P.D.   ASSURANCE

Knapp offered this tune to Crosby, who then wrote the text, crafting what has become an immensely popular
hymn among evangelical Christians. The *Psalter Hymnal* (1987) substituted Post's second stanza as a Reformed
theological "corrective" to Crosby's original "rapture" stanza.

186 When Peace like a River

1 When peace like a riv-er at-tend-eth my way, when
2 Though Sa-tan should buf-fet, though tri-als should come, let
3 My sin— oh, the bliss of this glo-ri-ous thought!— my
4 O Lord, haste the day when my faith shall be sight, the

sor-rows like sea bil-lows roll; what-ev-er my lot, thou hast
this blest as-sur-ance con-trol: that Christ has re-gard-ed my
sin, not in part, but the whole, is nailed to the cross, and I
clouds be rolled back as a scroll; the trump shall re-sound and the

taught me to say, "It is well, it is well with my soul."
help-less es-tate, and has shed his own blood for my soul.
bear it no more; praise the Lord, praise the Lord, O my soul!
Lord shall de-scend; e-ven so, it is well with my soul.

Refrain

It is well with my soul; it is well, it is well with my soul.
it is well with my soul;

Words: Horatio G. Spafford (1873), P.D.
Music: Philip P. Bliss (1876), P.D.

11 8 11 9 with refrain
VILLE DU HAVRE

Spafford wrote these reassuring words after his four daughters drowned in a ship collision in the mid-Atlantic. A friend of the family, Bliss composed the music and named the tune after the boat that perished. Text and music of this popular testimonial hymn were published in *Gospel Hymns No. 2* (1876), edited by Bliss and Ira Sankey.

Low in the Grave Christ Lay   187

Words and Music: Robert Lowry (1874), alt., P.D.

65 64 with refrain
CHRIST AROSE

Lowry's hymn features meditative stanzas to which the refrain responds with its dramatic phrases: "He arose!" A Baptist preacher and a teacher of rhetoric, Lowry is best known today for his gospel hymns and his compiling of gospel hymnals and Sunday school songbooks.

188 Sing Them Over Again to Me/ Wonderful Words of Life

1 Sing them o-ver a-gain to me, won-der-ful words of life;
2 Christ, the bless-ed one, gives to all won-der-ful words of life;
3 Sweet-ly ech-o the gos-pel call, won-der-ful words of life;

let me more of their beau-ty see, won-der-ful words of life.
sin-ner, list to the lov-ing call, won-der-ful words of life.
of-fer par-don and peace to all, won-der-ful words of life.

Refrain

Words of life and beau-ty, teach me faith and du-ty.
All so free-ly giv-en, woo-ing us to heaven. Beau-ti-ful words,
Je-sus, on-ly Sav-ior, sanc-ti-fy for-ev-er.

won-der-ful words, won-der-ful words of life. life.

Words and Music: Philip P. Bliss (1874), P.D.

86 86 66 with refrain
WORDS OF LIFE

This is one of Bliss' most memorable gospel songs, first published for use in Sunday schools. Here we encounter not only the Bible, which is the God's Word for our lives, but also Jesus, the very incarnate Word of God.

Man of Sorrows—What a Name   189

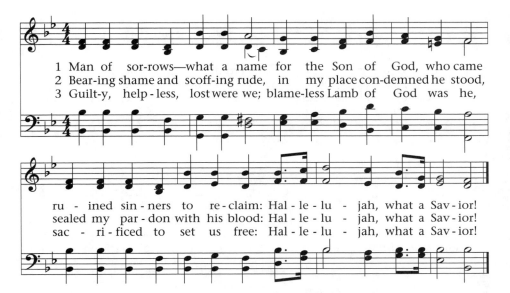

1 Man of sor-rows—what a name for the Son of God, who came
2 Bear-ing shame and scoff-ing rude, in my place con-demned he stood,
3 Guilt-y, help-less, lost were we; blame-less Lamb of God was he,

ru - ined sin-ners to re-claim: Hal - le - lu - jah, what a Sav-ior!
sealed my par-don with his blood: Hal - le - lu - jah, what a Sav-ior!
sac - ri-ficed to set us free: Hal - le - lu - jah, what a Sav-ior!

4 He was lifted up to die;
"It is finished" was his cry;
now in heaven exalted high:
Hallelujah, what a Savior!

5 When he comes, our glorious King,
all his ransomed home to bring,
then anew this song we'll sing:
Hallelujah, what a Savior!

Words and Music: Philip P. Bliss (1875), alt., P.D.

77 78
HALLELUJAH! WHAT A SAVIOR

The initial stanzas refer to Isaiah's depiction of the "suffering servant," but the text ends with Christ triumphant, returning to gather all his people into one throng to sing their "alleluias" to their Savior. Bliss wrote both text and tune just a year before his tragic death in a railway disaster at the beginning of his career as a singing evangelist and hymnal publisher.

190   To God Be the Glory

1 To God be the glo - ry, great things he has done; so loved he the
2 O per - fect re - demp-tion, the pur-chase of blood, to ev - ery be -
3 Great things he has taught us, great things he has done, and great our re -

world that he gave us his Son, who yield - ed his life an a -
liev - er the prom-ise of God; the vil - est of - fend - er who
joic - ing through Je - sus the Son; but pur - er and high - er and

tone-ment for sin, and o-pened the life - gate that we may go in.
tru - ly be - lieves, that mo-ment from Je - sus a par-don re - ceives.
great - er will be our won-der, our glad-ness,when Je - sus we see.

Refrain

Praise the Lord, praise the Lord; let the earth hear his voice! Praise the Lord,

Words: Fanny J. Crosby (1875), alt., P.D.
Music: William H. Doane (1875), P.D.

11 11 11 11 with refrain
TO GOD BE THE GLORY

praise the Lord; let the peo-ple re-joice! O come to the Fa-ther through

Je-sus the Son, and give him the glo-ry; great things he has done.

"Blessed Assurance" (185) and this text are among the best-known of the thousands of gospel song texts written by Crosby. However, these words focus on objective praise for God's mighty acts in Christ, and not on the personal experience themes more commonly associated with gospel hymns. Doane's cheerful music was composed for these words.

191 I Will Sing of My Redeemer

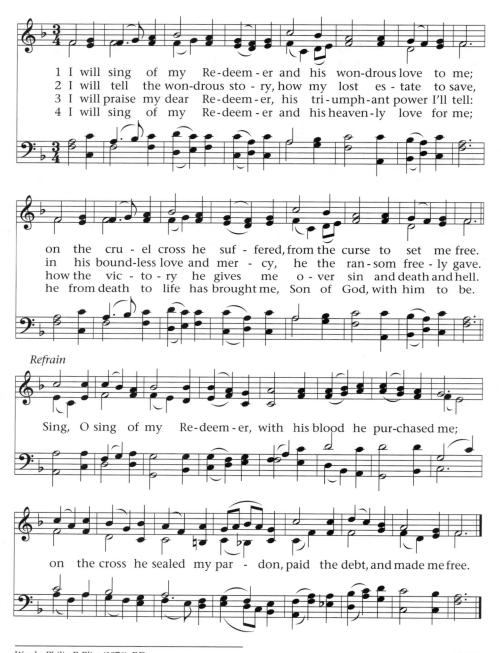

1 I will sing of my Re-deem-er and his won-drous love to me;
2 I will tell the won-drous sto-ry, how my lost es-tate to save,
3 I will praise my dear Re-deem-er, his tri-umph-ant power I'll tell;
4 I will sing of my Re-deem-er and his heaven-ly love for me;

on the cru-el cross he suf-fered, from the curse to set me free.
in his bound-less love and mer-cy, he the ran-som free-ly gave.
how the vic-to-ry he gives me o-ver sin and death and hell.
he from death to life has brought me, Son of God, with him to be.

Refrain

Sing, O sing of my Re-deem-er, with his blood he pur-chased me;

on the cross he sealed my par-don, paid the debt, and made me free.

Words: Philip P. Bliss (1876), P.D.
Music: Rowland H. Prichard (1830), P.D.

87 87 D
HYFRYDOL

This text was found among the belongings of Bliss after his tragic death in a train wreck when he was on his way to be the songleader for one of "Major" Whittle's crusades. Another musical associate of Whittle, James McGranaham, composed a gospel hymn setting for Bliss's text. But the setting provided here (from the 1987 *Psalter Hymnal*) unites this grand text about Christ's atonement with a well-loved Welsh tune (also used in this collection for "Love Divine…" (88) with an alternate harmonization).

Break Now the Bread of Life 192

1 Break now the bread of life, dear Lord, to me,
2 Bless your own word of truth, dear Lord, to me,
3 You are the bread of life, dear Lord, to me,
4 O send your Spir - it now, dear Lord, to me,

as once you broke the loaves be - side the sea.
as when you blessed the bread by Gal - i - lee.
your ho - ly Word the truth that res - cues me.
that he may touch my eyes and make me see.

Be - yond the sa - cred page I seek you, Lord;
Then shall all bond - age cease, all fet - ters fall;
Give me to eat and live with you a - bove;
Show me the truth made plain with - in your Word,

my spir - it waits for you, O liv - ing Word.
and I shall find my peace, my All in all.
teach me to love your truth, for you are love.
for in your book re - vealed I see you, Lord.

Words: st. 1-2, Mary A. Lathbury (1877), alt.; st. 3-4, Alexander Groves (1842-1909), P.D.
Music: William F. Sherwin (1877), P.D.

64 64 D
BREAD OF LIFE

Not a eucharistic hymn, this text draws on biblical images to depict Scripture's role in our lives, and serves as a sung prayer for illumination. This hymn comes from the Chautauqua Institution in upstate New York, a famous conference grounds for Bible study, training of Sunday school teachers, and concerts.

193 O Master, Let Me Walk with Thee

1 O Mas-ter, let me walk with thee in low-ly
2 Help me the slow of heart to move by some clear,
3 Teach me thy pa-tience; still with thee in clos-er,
4 In hope that sends a shin-ing ray far down the

paths of ser - vice free; tell me thy se - cret; help me
win-ning word of love; teach me the way-ward feet to
dear - er com - pa - ny, in work that keeps faith sweet and
fu - ture's broad-ening way, in peace that on - ly thou canst

bear the strain of toil, the fret of care.
stay, and guide them in the home - ward way.
strong, in trust that tri - umphs o - ver wrong.
give, with thee, O Mas - ter, let me live.

Words: Washington Gladden (1879), P.D.
Music: Henry Percy Smith (1874), P.D.

88 88
MARYTON

A strong proponent of the social gospel, Gladden intended his poem to be "an honest cry of human need" and a call for Christian service. It was soon revised as a hymn, and Gladden himself chose MARYTON as the appropriately gentle tune for his text, even though the opening couplet of each stanza is broken by the shorter melodic phrases of this tune.

I Know Not Why God's Wondrous Grace   194

1 I know not why God's won-drous grace to me he has made known,
2 I know not how this sav - ing faith to me he did im - part,
3 I know not how the Spir - it moves, con-vin-cing us of sin,
4 I know not what of good or ill may be re-served for me,

nor why, un-wor-thy, Christ in love re - deemed me for his own.
nor how be-liev-ing in his Word wrought peace with - in my heart.
re - veal-ing Je - sus through the Word, cre - a - ting faith in him.
of wea - ry ways or gold - en days, be - fore his face I see.

Refrain

But "I know whom I have be - liev-ed, and am per - suad-ed that he is

a-ble to keep that which I've com-mit-ted un-to him a-gainst that day."

Words: Daniel W. Whittle (1883); based on 2 Timothy 1:12, P.D.
Music: James McGranahan (1883), P.D.

86 86 with refrain
EL NATHAN

This gospel hymn explores the contrast between "I know not . . . " in the stanzas and the certainty of "I know . . . " in the refrain. A military man turned evangelist, "Major" Whittle wrote hymns under the pseudonym "El Nathan." The music was composed by one of Whittle's songleaders for his crusades, James McGranahan.

195 When We Walk with the Lord / Trust and Obey

1 When we walk with the Lord in the light of his Word, what a
2 But we nev-er can prove the de-lights of his love un-til
3 Then in fel-low-ship sweet we will sit at his feet, or we'll

glo-ry he sheds on our way! While we do his good will he a-
all on the al-tar we lay; for the fa-vor he shows and the
walk by his side in the way; what he says we will do, where he

bides with us still, and with all who will trust and o-bey.
joy he be-stows are for those who will trust and o-bey.
sends we will go— nev-er fear, on-ly trust and o-bey.

Refrain

Trust and o-bey, for there's no oth-er way to be

hap-py in Je-sus but to trust and o-bey.

Words: John H. Sammis (1887), P.D.
Music: Daniel B. Towner (1887), P.D.

669 D with refrain
TRUST AND OBEY

At a Moody crusade, Towner overheard a convert say he would "trust and obey." Towner sent that phrase to Sammis, who first penned those words into the refrain and then wrote the stanzas, whereupon Towner crafted the music. The hymn became widely popular due to its use in the Moody-Sankey crusades and publication in the Sankey hymnals.

Lead On, O King Eternal 196

1 Lead on, O King e - ter - nal, the day of march has come;
2 Lead on, O King e - ter - nal, till sin's fierce war shall cease,
3 Lead on, O King e - ter - nal; we fol - low, not with fears,

hence-forth in fields of con - quest your tents will be our home.
and ho - li - ness shall whis - per the sweet a - men of peace.
for glad-ness breaks like morn - ing wher - e'er your face ap - pears.

Through days of prep - a - ra - tion your grace has made us strong;
For not with swords' loud clash - ing or roll of stir-ring drums—
Your cross is lift - ed o'er us, we jour-ney in its light;

and now, O King e - ter - nal, we lift our bat - tle song.
with deeds of love and mer - cy the heav-enly king-dom comes.
the crown a - waits the con - quest; lead on, O God of might.

Words: Ernest W. Shurtleff (1888), alt., P.D.
Music: Henry T. Smart (1836), P.D.

76 76 D
LANCASHIRE

Written as a commencement poem, Shurtleff's text is initially laced with war imagery but then fortunately moves to the biblical images of "deeds of love and mercy" in Christian service and eschatological hope. Smart's rousing march tune fits the text well; note particularly the musical animation in the third phrase.

197 Lift Every Voice and Sing

1 Lift ev-ery voice and sing   till earth and heav - en   ring,
2 Ston-y the road we trod,   bit - ter the chast-ening   rod,
3 God of our wea - ry years,   God of our si - lent   tears,

ring with the har - mon - ies of lib - er - ty;
felt in the days when hope un - born had died;
thou who hast brought us thus far on the way;

let our re - joic-ing rise, high as the lis - tening skies,
yet with a stead - y beat, have not our wea - ry feet
thou who hast, by thy might, led us in - to the light,

let it re-sound loud as the roll - ing sea.
come to the place for which our peo - ple sighed?
keep us for - ev - er in the path, we pray.

Words: James Weldon Johnson (1900), alt., P.D.
Music: J. Rosamond Johnson (1900), P.D.

12 10 12 10 14 14 12 10
LIFT EVERY VOICE

Sing a song full of the faith that the dark past has taught us,
We have come o - ver a way that with tears has been wa-tered;
Lest our feet stray from the plac - es, our God, where we met thee,

sing a song full of the hope that the pres - ent has
we have come, tread - ing our path through the blood of the
lest, our hearts drunk with the wine of the world, we for -

brought us; fac - ing the ris - ing sun of our new day be -
slaugh - tered, out from the gloom - y past, till now we stand at
get thee; shad-owed be - neath thy hand, may we for - ev - er

gun, let us march on till vict - o - ry is won.
last where the white gleam of our bright star is cast.
stand, true to our God, true to our na - tive land.

Originally written for a birthday anniversary of Abraham Lincoln by the African-American brothers James W. and J. Rosamond Johnson, this hymn became the theme song of the National Association for the Advancement of Colored People (NAACP). It was much used in the Civil Rights movement and today is recognized as the anthem of African-Americans; many others have also adopted it.

198   This Is My Father's World

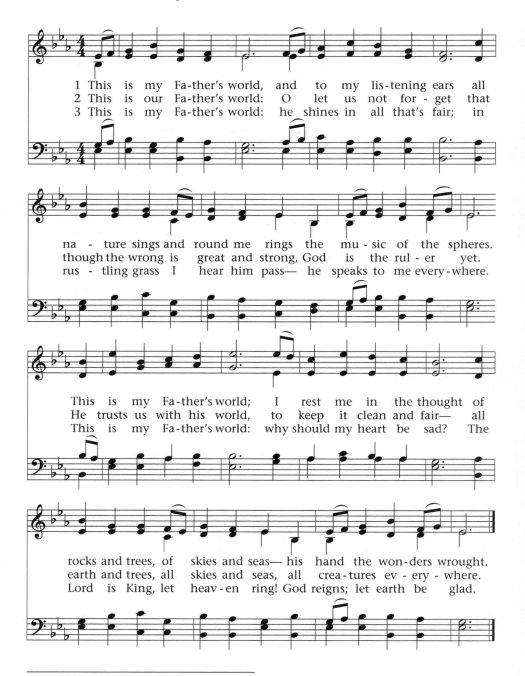

1 This is my Fa-ther's world, and to my lis-tening ears all
2 This is our Fa-ther's world: O let us not for-get that
3 This is my Fa-ther's world: he shines in all that's fair; in

na - ture sings and round me rings the mu - sic of the spheres.
though the wrong is great and strong, God is the rul - er yet.
rus - tling grass I hear him pass— he speaks to me every-where.

This is my Fa-ther's world; I rest me in the thought of
He trusts us with his world, to keep it clean and fair— all
This is my Fa-ther's world: why should my heart be sad? The

rocks and trees, of skies and seas— his hand the won-ders wrought.
earth and trees, all skies and seas, all crea-tures ev - ery - where.
Lord is King, let heav-en ring! God reigns; let earth be glad.

Words: Maltbie D. Babcock (1901), alt.; st. 2 rev. Mary Babcock Crawford (1972), P.D.   66 86 D
Music: English; adapt. Franklin L. Sheppard (1915), P.D.   TERRA BEATA

Babcock's text helps us confess that all creation is the handiwork of God; Babcock's granddaughter revised stanza 2 to bring greater ecological responsibility into focus. A friend of the elder Babcock, Sheppard adapted a traditional English folk tune of which a variant had already appeared in the *English Hymnal* (1906).

Have Thine Own Way, Lord 199

1 Have thine own way, Lord! Have thine own way!
2 Have thine own way, Lord! Have thine own way!
3 Have thine own way, Lord! Have thine own way!
4 Have thine own way, Lord! Have thine own way!

Thou art the pot - ter, I am the clay.
Search me and try me, Mas - ter, to - day.
Wound - ed and wea - ry, help me, I pray.
Hold o'er my be - ing ab - so - lute sway.

Mold me and make me af - ter thy will,
O - pen mine eyes, my sin show me now,
Pow - er, all pow - er, sure - ly is thine.
Fill with thy Spir - it till all shall see

while I am wait - ing, yield - ed and still.
as in thy pres - ence hum - bly I bow.
Touch me and heal me, Sav - ior di - vine.
Christ on - ly, al - ways, liv - ing in me.

Words: Adelaide A. Pollard (1901), P.D.
Music: George C. Stebbins (1907), P.D.

99 99
ADELAIDE

Inspired by the potter imagery in Jeremiah 18:6 and Isaiah 64:8, Pollard wrote this sung prayer for consecration to God's will in our lives. Stebbins composed the tune for her text; they appeared together in a Stebbins hymnal, and the hymn was made popular by Ira Sankey in the Dwight Moody crusades.

200 We Praise You, O God

1 We praise you, O God, our Re - deem - er, Cre - a - tor;
2 We wor - ship you, God of our fa - thers and moth-ers;
3 With voic - es u - nit - ed our prais - es we of - fer;

in grate - ful de - vo - tion our trib - ute we bring.
through life's storm and tem - pest our guide you have been.
our songs of thanks-giv - ing to you we now raise.

We lay it be - fore you, we kneel and a - dore you;
When per - ils o'er - take us, you nev - er for-sake us.
Your strong arm will guide us, our God is be - side us.

we bless your ho - ly name, glad prais - es we sing.
And with your help, O Lord, our bat - tles we win.
To you, our great Re - deem - er, for - e'er be praise!

Words: Julia C. Cory (1902), alt., P.D.
Music: Adrianus Valerius, *Nederlandtsch Gedenckclanck* (1626), P.D.

12 11 12 11
KREMSER

Asked to write new words for the KREMSER tune (see "We Gather Together" [54]), Cady penned this text. It has become a great hymn for Thanksgiving services—one which not only praises God for his redemptive care of our lives in the past but also expresses confidence in God's providence for future years.

Where Cross the Crowded Ways of Life   201

1 Where cross the crowd-ed ways of life, where sound the
2 In haunts of wretch-ed-ness and need, on shad-owed
3 The cup of wa-ter given for you still holds the
4 O Mas-ter, from the moun-tain-side make haste to

cries of race and clan, a-bove the noise of
thresh-olds dark with fears, from paths where hide the
fresh-ness of your grace; yet long these mul-ti-
heal these hearts of pain; a-mong these rest-less

self - ish strife, we hear your voice, O Son of Man.
lures of greed, we catch the vi - sion of your tears.
tudes to see the true com-pas-sion of your face.
throngs a-bide, and tread the cit - y's streets a-gain—

5 till all the world shall learn your love
and follow where your feet have trod,
till glorious from your heaven above
shall come the city of our God.

Words: Frank M. North (1905), alt., P.D.   88 88
Music: Wwilliam Gardiner's *Sacred Melodies* (1815), P.D.   GERMANY

This is one of the earliest and finest of the "city" hymns, whose text was written by a Methodist churchman rooted in New York City. Having met both Haydn and Beethoven on his business travels, Gardiner cobbled together several musical phrases from Beethoven and Mozart to fashion this particular tune.

202 Joyful, Joyful, We Adore Thee

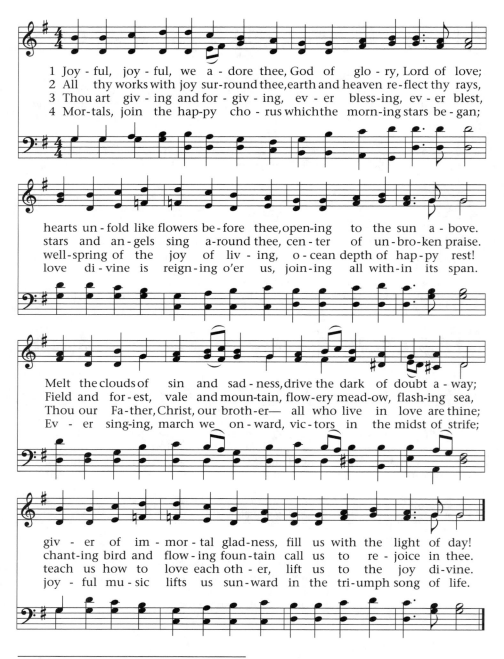

1 Joy - ful, joy - ful, we a - dore thee, God of glo - ry, Lord of love;
2 All thy works with joy sur - round thee, earth and heaven re - flect thy rays,
3 Thou art giv - ing and for - giv - ing, ev - er bless - ing, ev - er blest,
4 Mor - tals, join the hap - py cho - rus which the morn - ing stars be - gan;

hearts un - fold like flowers be - fore thee, open - ing to the sun a - bove.
stars and an - gels sing a - round thee, cen - ter of un - bro - ken praise.
well - spring of the joy of liv - ing, o - cean depth of hap - py rest!
love di - vine is reign - ing o'er us, join - ing all with - in its span.

Melt the clouds of sin and sad - ness, drive the dark of doubt a - way;
Field and for - est, vale and moun - tain, flow - ery mead - ow, flash - ing sea,
Thou our Fa - ther, Christ, our broth - er— all who live in love are thine;
Ev - er sing - ing, march we on - ward, vic - tors in the midst of strife;

giv - er of im - mor - tal glad - ness, fill us with the light of day!
chant - ing bird and flow - ing foun - tain call us to re - joice in thee.
teach us how to love each oth - er, lift us to the joy di - vine.
joy - ful mu - sic lifts us sun - ward in the tri - umph song of life.

Words: Henry Van Dyke (1911), alt., P.D.
Music: Ludwig van Beethoven (1824); arr. Edward Hodges (1864), P.D.

87 87 D
HYMN TO JOY

Inspired by Beethoven's choral Symphony No. 9 (which uses the "Ode to Joy" text by Schiller) and by the Berk-shire mountains in Massachusetts, van Dyke transformed Schiller's humanistic poem into a hymn of joy to God. The original phrase "brother-love binds man to man" in stanza 4 has been much altered in modern hymnals.

The King Shall Come When Morning Dawns 203

1 The King shall come when morning dawns and
2 not, as of old, a little child, to
3 Oh, brighter than the rising morn when
4 oh, brighter than that glorious morn shall

light triumphant breaks, when beauty gilds the
bear and fight and die, but crowned with glory
Christ, victorious, rose and left the lonesome
dawn upon our race the day when Christ in

eastern hills and life to joy awakes—
like the sun that lights the morning sky.
place of death, despite the rage of foes—
splendor comes and we shall see his face.

5 The King shall come when morning dawns
   and light and beauty brings.
   Hail, Christ the Lord! Your people pray:
   come quickly, King of kings.

Words: John Brownlie (1907), alt., P.D.
Music: John Wyeth's, *Repository of Sacred Music* (1813); harm. Jack Grotenhuis,
   1983 © 1987 Faith Alive Christian Resources

CM
MORNING SONG

A Scottish Presbyterian pastor and translator of Greek and Latin hymns, Brownlie infused his Advent text with images of light that are typical of early Greek hymns. The tune comes from the Appalachian region of the United States and appears in various shape-note hymnals in the first half of the nineteenth century.

204 On a Hill Far Away/
The Old Rugged Cross

1 On a hill far a-way stood an old rug-ged cross,
2 O that old rug-ged cross, so de-spised by the world,
3 In the old rug-ged cross, stained with blood so di-vine,
4 To that old rug-ged cross I will ev - er be true,

the em - blem of suf - fering and shame;
has a won - drous at - trac - tion for me;
a won - drous beau - ty I see;
its shame and re - proach glad - ly bear;

and I love that old cross where the dear - est and best
for the dear Lamb of God left his glo - ry a - bove
for 'twas on that old cross Je - sus suf - fered and died,
then he'll call me some - day to my home far a - way,

for a world of lost sin - ners was slain.
to bear it to dark Cal - va - ry.
to par - don and sanc - ti - fy me.
where his glo - ry for - ev - er I'll share.

Words and Music: George Bennard (1913), P.D.

Irregular with refrain
OLD RUGGED CROSS

Refrain

So, I'll cher - ish the old rug - ged cross, till my
cross, the old rug - ged cross,

tro - phies at last I lay down; I will cling to the old rug - ged
cross, the

cross, and ex - change it some day for a crown.
old rug - ged cross,

Decried by theologians for the text's veneration of the cross (as opposed to worship of Christ who died on the cross), but much loved by many evangelical Christians (according to popularity polls on favorite hymns), Bennard's gospel song is a sung crucifix whose literary and musical qualities pale in comparison to "Lift High the Cross" (162).

205 In Christ There Is No East or West

1 In Christ there is no east or west, in
2 In him shall true hearts ev - ery - where their
3 Join hands, then, peo - ple of the faith, what -
4 In Christ now meet both east and west, in

him no south or north, but one great fam - i -
high com - mu - nion find; his ser - vice is the
e'er your race may be; all chil - dren of the
him meet south and north; all Christ - like souls are

ly of love through - out the whole wide earth.
gold - en cord close bind - ing hu - man - kind.
liv - ing God are sure - ly kin to me.
one in him through - out the whole wide earth.

Words: William A. Dunkerly (1908), alt., P.D.   86 86
Music: Afro-American spiritual (19th c.); adapt. and harm. Harry T. Burleigh (1939), P.D.   MCKEE

Written under Dunkerley's pseudonym "John Oxenham," this text celebrates the grand scope of Christ's world-wide church. What is now considered male language in the original text has been altered variously in modern hymnals; our version here is one example. MCKEE was originally an Irish tune adopted by African-Americans, which Burleigh then united to this text in *The Hymnal* 1940.

Infant Holy, Infant Lowly 206

1 In-fant ho-ly, in-fant low-ly, for his bed a cat-tle stall;
2 Flocks were sleep-ing, shep-herds keep-ing vig-il till the morn-ing new

ox-en low-ing, lit-tle know-ing Christ the child is Lord of all.
saw the glo-ry, heard the sto-ry, tid-ings of a gos-pel true.

Swift-ly wing-ing an-gels sing-ing, bells are ring-ing, tid-ings bring-ing:
Thus re-joic-ing, free from sor-row, prais-es voic-ing, greet the mor-row:

Christ the child is Lord of all! Christ the child is Lord of all!
Christ the child was born for you! Christ the child was born for you!

Words: Polish "W Zlobie Lezy," tr. Edith M. G. Reed (1921), P.D.   87 87 88 77
Music: Polish; harm. *Psalter Hymnal* (1987), © 1987, Faith Alive Christian Resources   W ZLOBIE LEZY

Thought to date from the thirteenth or fourteenth century, this folksy carol provides vignettes from the Christmas story in short phrases and tight rhymes. The music, which has similar short phrases, bears the rhythmic pattern of the mazurka, a Polish dance.

207 Great Is Thy Faithfulness

1 Great is thy faith - ful - ness, O God my Fa - ther;
2 Sum - mer and win - ter and spring - time and har - vest,
3 Par - don for sin and a peace that en - dur - eth,

there is no shad - ow of turn - ing with thee;
sun, moon, and stars in their cours - es a - bove
thy own dear pres - ence to cheer and to guide,

thou chang - est not, thy com - pas - sions, they fail not;
join with all na - ture in man - i - fold wit - ness
strength for to - day and bright hope for to - mor - row—

as thou hast been thou for - ev - er wilt be.
to thy great faith - ful - ness, mer - cy, and love.
bless - ings all mine, with ten thou - sand be - side!

Words: Thomas O. Chisholm (1923)
Music: William M. Runyan (1923)
Words and Music © 1923, Renewed 1951 Hope Publishing Company

11 10 11 10 with refrain
FAITHFULNESS

Great is thy faith-ful-ness! Great is thy faith-ful-ness!

Morn - ing by morn - ing new mer - cies I see;

all I have need - ed thy hand hath pro - vid - ed.

Great is thy faith - ful-ness, Lord, un - to me!

Inspired in part by the comforting words of Lamentations 3:22-23, Chisholm wrote this text to express his daily realization of God's covenant faithfulness, and then asked Runyan to compose a tune for it. The hymn gained much popularity throughout the English-speaking world through its use in Billy Graham crusades.

208 Good Christians All, Rejoice and Sing

1 Good Chris-tians all, re-joice and sing! Now is the tri - umph
2 The Lord of life is risen to - day. Sing songs of praise a -
3 Praise we in songs of vic - to - ry that love, that life which
4 Your name we bless, O ris - en Lord, and sing to - day with

of our King! To all the world glad news we bring:
long his way. Let all the world re - joice and say:
can-not die, and sing with hearts up - lift - ed high:
one ac - cord the life laid down, the life re - stored:

Refrain

Al - le - lu - ia, al - le - lu - ia, al - le - lu - ia!

Words: Cyril A. Alington (1925), alt. © 1958, renewed 1986 Hymns Ancient & Modern, Ltd.
(Admin. Hope Publishing).
Music: Melchior Vulpius (1609), P.D.

888 with alleluias

GELOBT SEI GOTT

Alington wrote this fine text for Vulpius' exuberant tune, first published together in *Songs of Praise* (1931). The excitement of the Easter message is ably expressed in the fervor and syncopations of the melody.

May the Mind of Christ, My Savior 209

1 May the mind of Christ, my Sav-ior, live in me from day to day,
2 May the word of God dwell rich-ly in my heart from hour to hour,
3 May the peace of God, my Fa-ther, rule my life in ev-ery-thing,

by his love and power con-trol-ling all I do and say.
so that all may see I tri-umph on-ly through his power.
that I may be calm to com-fort sick and sor-row-ing.

4 May the love of Jesus fill me
   as the waters fill the sea.
   Him exalting, self abasing:
   this is victory.

5 May we run the race before us,
   strong and brave to face the foe,
   looking only unto Jesus
   as we onward go.

Words: Kate B. Wilkinson (1925), P.D.
Music: A. Cyril Barham-Gould (1925), P.D.

87 85
ST. LEONARD'S

Inspired by Philippians 2:5 and Hebrews 12:1-2, Wilkinson gives us a catalogue hymn in which we pray for the mind and love of Jesus and the word and peace of God to fill us in our earthly journey. The tune was written for this text; the tune title refers to the British town St. Leonards-on-Sea, named after the fifth-century Leonard of Limosin, the patron saint of pregnant women and prisoners of war.

210 Spirit of the Living God

1 Spir-it of the liv-ing God, fall a-fresh on me;
2 Spir-it of the liv-ing God, move a-mong us all;

Spir-it of the liv-ing God, fall a-fresh on me.
make us one in heart and mind, make us one in love;

Melt me, mold me, fill me, use me.
hum-ble, car-ing, self-less, shar-ing.

Spir-it of the liv-ing God, fall a-fresh on me.
Spir-it of the liv-ing God, fill our lives with love.

Words: st. 1, Daniel Iverson (1926) © 1935, 1963 Birdwing Music (admin. by EMI CMG Publishing) (ASCAP).
st. 2, Michael Baughen © 1982 Hope Publishing Company   irregular
Music: Daniel Iverson, 1926. © 1935, 1963 Birdwing Music (admin. by EMI CMB Publishing (ASCAP).   IVERSON

A fervent prayer for the Holy Spirit, this hymn combines the original chorus words and music by the church planter Iverson with a more recent stanza by Baughen, the founder of the Jubilate Group in England. He was an editor of *Hymns for Today's Church* (1982) in which this composite hymn was first published.

God of Grace and God of Glory   211

1 God of grace and God of glo-ry, on your peo-ple
2 Lo! the hosts of e-vil round us scorn the Christ, as-
3 Cure your chil-dren's war-ring mad-ness; bend our pride to
4 Save us from weak res-ig-na-tion to the e-vils

pour your power; crown your an-cient Chur-ch's sto-ry,
sail his ways! From the fears that long have bound us
your con-trol; shame our wan-ton, self-ish glad-ness,
we de-plore; let the gift of your sal-va-tion

bring its bud to glo-rious flower. Grant us wis-dom, grant us cour-age
free our hearts to faith and praise. Grant us wis-dom, grant us cour-age
rich in things and poor in soul. Grant us wis-dom, grant us cour-age,
be our glo-ry ev-er-more. Grant us wis-dom, grant us cour-age,

for the fac-ing of this hour, for the fac-ing of this hour.
for the liv-ing of these days, for the liv-ing of these days.
lest we miss your king-dom's goal, lest we miss your king-dom's goal.
serv-ing you whom we a-dore, serv-ing you whom we a-dore.

Words: Harry E. Fosdick (1930), alt., P.D.
Music: John Hughes (1905); harm. Henry V. Gerike (2006) © Concordia Publishing House

87 87 877
CWM RHONDDA

Committed to the social gospel, Fosdick wrote this text as an "urgent personal prayer" for wisdom and courage to be used for the dedication of Riverside Church at the edge of Harlem in New York City. Though Fosdick never appreciated the union, his text and this great tune were enduringly united in the *Methodist Hymnal* (1935). For the tune, see "Guide Me, O My Great Redeemer" (101).

212 Lord of All Hopefulness

Unison

1 Lord of all hope-ful-ness, Lord of all joy,
2 Lord of all ea-ger-ness, Lord of all faith,
3 Lord of all kind-li-ness, Lord of all grace,
4 Lord of all gen-tle-ness, Lord of all calm,

whose trust, ev-er child-like, no cares could de-stroy:
whose strong hands were skilled at the plane and the lathe:
your hands swift to wel-come, your arms to em-brace:
whose voice is con-tent-ment, whose pres-ence is balm:

be there at our wak-ing, and give us, we pray,
be there at our la-bors, and give us, we pray,
be there at our hom-ing, and give us, we pray,
be there at our sleep-ing, and give us, we pray,

your bliss in our hearts, Lord, at the break of the day.
your strength in our hearts, Lord, at the noon of the day.
your love in our hearts, Lord, at the eve of the day.
your peace in our hearts, Lord, at the end of the day.

Words: Jan Struther from *England Songs of Praise* (1931). Reproduced by permission of
Oxford University Press.
Music: trad. Irish folk melody; harm. *Hymnal 1982* © Church Publishing, Inc.

10 11 11 12

SLANE

This is an "all-day" prayer, invoking God's blessings for waking, working, homecoming, and sleeping. It was
written by Joyce Torrens, whose pseudonym was Jan Struther. SLANE first became a hymn tune when wed with
"Be Thou My Vision" (32) in the *Church Hymnary* (1927); it was joined to Struther's text in *Song of Praise* (1931).

Precious Lord, Take My Hand 213

1 Pre - cious Lord, take my hand, lead me on, help me stand;
2 When my way grows_ drear, pre - cious Lord, lin - ger near;
3 When the dark - ness ap - pears and the night draws_ near,

I am tired, I am weak, I am worn; through the
when my life is_ al - most_ gone, hear my
when the day is_ past and_ gone, at the

storm, through the night, lead me on to the light;
cry, hear my call, hold my hand lest I fall;
riv - er I stand, guide my feet, hold my hand;

take my hand, pre - cious Lord, lead me home.

Words: Thomas A. Dorsey (1932)
Music: George N. Allen, 1844; adapt. Thomas A. Dorsey, 1938
Words and Music © 1938 (Renewed) WARNER-TAMERLANE Publishing Corp.

irregular
PRECIOUS LORD

Dorsey wrote this text following the death of his wife and their newborn son. He adapted an old hymn-tune, MAITLAND, by Oberlin professor George Allen, to fit his Old Testament lament-style text. Dorsey is considered the "father" of Black gospel hymnody and had a distinguished career as a composer and conductor.

214 I Serve a Risen Savior/He Lives, He Lives

1 I serve a ris - en Sav - ior, he's in the world to - day;
2 In all the world a - round me I see his lov - ing care,
3 Re - joice, re - joice, O Chris - tian, lift up your voice and sing

I know that he is liv - ing, what - ev - er peo - ple say;
and though my heart grows wea - ry, I nev - er will de - spair;
e - ter - nal hal - le - lu - jahs to Je - sus Christ the King!

I see his hand of mer - cy, I hear his voice of cheer,
I know that he is lead - ing through all the storm - y blast;
The hope of all who seek him, the help of all who find;

and ev - ery time I need him he's al - ways near.
the day of his ap - pear - ing will come at last.
no oth - er is so lov - ing, so good and kind.

Words and Music: Alfred H. Ackley (1933) © 1933 Word Music, LLC.

76 76 76 74 with refrain
ACKLEY

Responding to the question "Why should I worship a dead Jew?" and no doubt inspired by Paul's stress on Christ's resurrection in 1 Corinthians 15, Ackley confesses here his personal experience with the living Christ. Both text and tune were published in *Triumphant Service Songs* (1933), issued by the Rodeheaver Publishing Company for which Ackley worked as an editor.

215 By the Sea of Crystal

1 By the sea of crys - tal, saints in glo - ry stand,
2 Out of trib - u - la - tion, death, and Sa - tan's hand,
3 "Un - to God Al - might - y, sit - ting on the throne,

myr - i - ad in num - ber, drawn from ev - ery land.
they have been trans - lat - ed, at the Lord's com - mand.
and the Lamb, vic - to - rious, be the praise a - lone."

Robed in white ap - par - el, washed in Je - sus' blood,
In their hands they're hold - ing palms of vic - to - ry.
God has wrought sal - va - tion; he did won - drous things.

they now reign in heav - en with the Lamb of God.
Hark! the ju - bilant cho - rus shouts tri - um - phant - ly.
Who shall not ex - tol thee, ho - ly King of kings!

Words: William Kuipers (1933); based on Revelation 4-5, P.D.
Music: John Vanderhoven (1933), P.D.

65 65 D
CRYSTAL

Hallowed as a theme song for the Christian Reformed Church's radio ministry "The Back to God Hour" from the 1950s to the 1970s, this hymn is the work of a CRC preacher and a CRC organist. It was first published in the then-new *Psalter Hymnal* (1934).

We Come, O Christ, to You 216

1 We come, O Christ, to you, true Son of God and man,
2 You are the way to God, your blood our ran - som paid;
3 You are the liv - ing truth; all wis - dom dwells in you,

by whom all things con - sist, in whom all life be - gan.
in you we face our Judge and Mak - er un - a - fraid.
the source of ev - ery skill, the one e - ter - nal True!

In you a - lone we live and move
Be - fore the throne ab - solved we stand;
O great I AM! in you we rest,

and have our be - ing in your love.
your love has met your law's de - mand.
sure an - swer to our ev - ery quest.

4 You only are true life—
  to know you is to live
  the more abundant life that
  earth can never give.
  O risen Lord! we live in you:
  in us each day your life renew!

5 We worship you, Lord Christ,
  our Savior and our King;
  to you our youth and strength
  adoringly we bring:
  so fill our hearts that all may view
  your life in us and turn to you!

Words: Margaret Clarkson (1946, revised 1984) © 1957, renewed 1985 and this trans.
© 2009 Hope Publishing Company. All rights reserved. Used by permission.
Music: James V. Lee (1951) © 1959 United Reformed Church

66 66 88

EASTVIEW

This Canadian text is a hymn of praise to Christ who is "the life, the way, and the truth." Clarkson wrote these words for the first InterVarsity Christian Fellowship convention in Toronto in 1946. The majestic tune came later from an English church organist who was variously a college bursar and a master magician.

217 Let All Things Now Living

1 Let all things now liv-ing a song of thanks-giv-ing to
2 His law he en-forc-es; the stars in their cours-es and

God the Cre - a-tor tri - um-phant-ly raise, who fash-ioned and
sun in its or-bit o - be-dient-ly shine; the hills and the

made us, pro - tect-ed and stayed us, who guides us and
moun-tains, the riv-ers and foun-tains, the deeps of the

leads to the end of our days. His ban - ners are o'er us, his
o - cean pro-claim him di-vine. We too should be voic-ing our

light goes be - fore us, a pil-lar of fire shin-ing forth in the
love and re - joic-ing; with glad ad - o - ra-tion a song let us

Words: Katherine K. Davis (1939) © 1939, 1966 E. C. Schirmer Music Co.,
  a division of ECS Publishing. Boston, MA.
Music: trad. Welsh harp melody, *Bardic Museum*, London (1802), P.D.

66 11 66 11 D

ASH GROVE

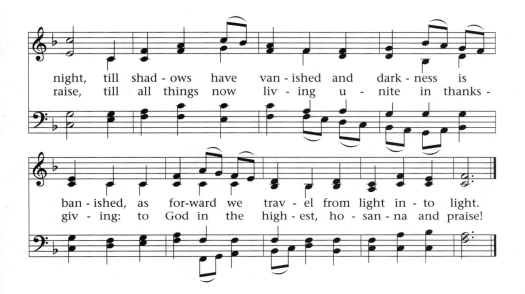

night, till shad-ows have van-ished and dark-ness is
raise, till all things now liv-ing u – nite in thanks-

ban-ished, as for-ward we trav – el from light in - to light.
giv – ing: to God in the high-est, ho - san - na and praise!

Employing Old Testament imagery, Davis' text helps us join in the praise of God from all his creatures;
it was written for the secular ASH GROVE melody, for which Davis also composed a fine descant that many
modern hymnals print.

218   O Lord My God/How Great Thou Art

1 O   Lord   my   God,   when   I   in   awe-some won-der
2 When through the   woods   and   for-est glades I   wan-der,
3 But   when   I   think   that God, his   Son not   spar-ing,
4 When Christ shall come,   with shout of   ac - cla - ma-tion,

con - sid - er   all   the works thy hand hath made,
I   hear the   birds   sing sweet-ly in   the   trees;
sent him   to   die,   I   scarce can take it   in,
and claim his   own,   what joy shall fill   my   heart!

I   see the   stars,   I   hear the might-y   thun-der,
when I   look down   from loft-y moun-tain gran-deur
that on the   cross,   my   bur-den glad-ly bear-ing,
Then I   shall bow   in   hum-ble ad - o - ra-tion

thy   power through-out   the   u - ni-verse dis-played;
and   hear the   brook   and feel the gen-tle breeze;
he   bled and   died   to   take a-way my   sin;
and   there pro-claim,   "My God, how great thou art!"

Words: Stuart K. Hine (1949)
Music: Swedish; harm. Stuart K. Hine (1949)
Words and Music © 1953 S. K. Hine. Renewed 1981. Administrator: Manna Music, Inc.

11 10 11 10 with refrain

Refrain

Then sings my soul, my Sav-ior God, to thee: how great thou art,

how great thou art! Then sings my soul, my Sav-ior God, to thee:

how great thou art, how great thou art!

Stuart K. Hine wrote English lyrics to the tune of an old Swedish melody, which is now commonly known as How Great Thou Art. The hymn gained much popularity through its singing by George B. Shea in the Billy Graham Crusades.

219 Lead Me, Guide Me

Lead me, guide me, a-long the way, for if you lead me, I can-not stray. Lord, let me walk each day with you, lead me my whole life through.

irregular
LEAD ME

Stanzas

1 I am weak and I need your strength and power
2 Help me walk in the paths of right - eous - ness;
3 I am lost if you take your hand from me,

to en - dure with grace___ my weak - est hour.
be my aid when Sa - tan and sin op - press.
I am blind with - out___ your light to see.

Help me through the dark - ness your face to see.
I am trust - ing you___ what - e'er may be.
Lord, for - ev - er may I your ser - vant be.

To Refrain

Lead me, O Lord, lead me.

A psalmodic prayer for guidance, Akers' hymn is representative of a mid-twentieth-century group of Black gospel songs by African-American composers who delighted in improvisational piano accompaniment. This is one of her songs that gained popularity in many diverse Christian communities when she published it through Manna Music.

220 Thy Strong Word

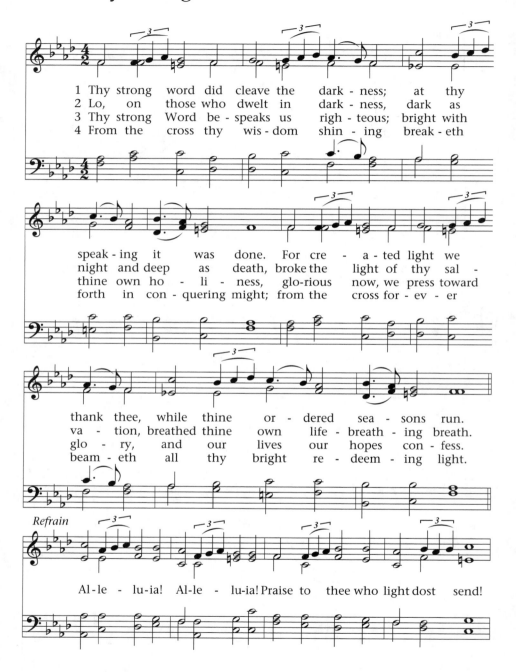

1 Thy strong word did cleave the dark - ness; at thy
2 Lo, on those who dwelt in dark - ness, dark as
3 Thy strong Word be - speaks us righ - teous; bright with
4 From the cross thy wis - dom shin - ing break - eth

speak - ing it was done. For cre - a - ted light we
night and deep as death, broke the light of thy sal -
thine own ho - li - ness, glo-rious now, we press toward
forth in con - quering might; from the cross for - ev - er

thank thee, while thine or - dered sea - sons run.
va - tion, breathed thine own life - breath - ing breath.
glo - ry, and our lives our hopes con - fess.
beam - eth all thy bright re - deem - ing light.

Refrain

Al - le - lu - ia! Al - le - lu - ia! Praise to thee who light dost send!

Words: Martin H. Franzmann (1954)
Music: Thomas J. Williams (1890); arr. Richard W. Hillert (1969)
Words and arr. © 1969 Concordia Publishing House

87 87 D
EBENEZER

Al-le - lu-ia! Al-le - lu - ia! Al-le - lu - ia with - out end!

5 Give us lips to sing thy glory,
  tongues thy mercy to proclaim,
  throats that shout the hope that fills us,
  mouths to speak thy holy name.
  Alleluia! Alleluia!
  May the light which thou dost send
  fill our songs with alleluias,
  alleluias without end!

6 God the Father, light-creator,
  to thee laud and honor be.
  To thee, Light of Light begotten,
  praise be sung eternally.
  Holy Spirit, light-revealer,
  glory, glory be to thee.
  Mortals, angels, now and ever
  praise the holy Trinity!

This is often thought to be the finest of the hymn texts by Franzmann, a Lutheran New Testament scholar in the
United States and England, who wrote these words for Concordia Seminary's commencement in 1954 in St. Louis.
The fine Welsh tune EBENEZER is given here in F minor; for "O the Deep, Deep Love of Jesus" (159) it is in E
minor.

221 Here, O Lord, Your Servants Gather

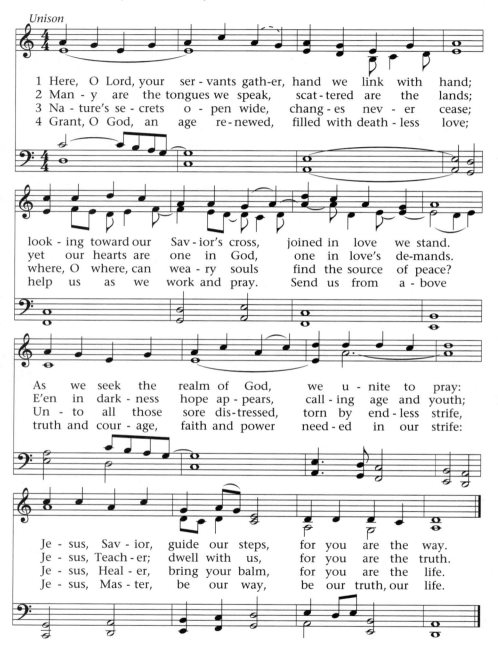

Unison

1 Here, O Lord, your ser-vants gath-er, hand we link with hand;
2 Man-y are the tongues we speak, scat-tered are the lands;
3 Na-ture's se-crets o-pen wide, chang-es nev-er cease;
4 Grant, O God, an age re-newed, filled with death-less love;

look-ing toward our Sav-ior's cross, joined in love we stand.
yet our hearts are one in God, one in love's de-mands.
where, O where, can wea-ry souls find the source of peace?
help us as we work and pray. Send us from a-bove

As we seek the realm of God, we u-nite to pray:
E'en in dark-ness hope ap-pears, call-ing age and youth;
Un-to all those sore dis-tressed, torn by end-less strife,
truth and cour-age, faith and power need-ed in our strife:

Je-sus, Sav-ior, guide our steps, for you are the way.
Je-sus, Teach-er; dwell with us, for you are the truth.
Je-sus, Heal-er, bring your balm, for you are the life.
Je-sus, Mas-ter, be our way, be our truth, our life.

Words: Tokuo Yamaguchi (1958); tr. Everett M. Stowe © 1958 The United Methodist
Publishing House (admin. the Copyright Company)
Music: Japanese Gagaku mode; arr. Isao Koizumi (1958) ©. Used by permission of JASRAC.

75 75 D

TOKYO

This Japanese hymn was inspired by Jesus' statement, "I am the way, the truth, and the life" (John 14:6), which was the theme of a Christian education conference held in Tokyo in 1958 for which this song was written and then sung in both Japanese and English. The melody draws on traditional Japanese court music, harmonized by one of Japan's outstanding hymnologists.

O God of Every Nation 222

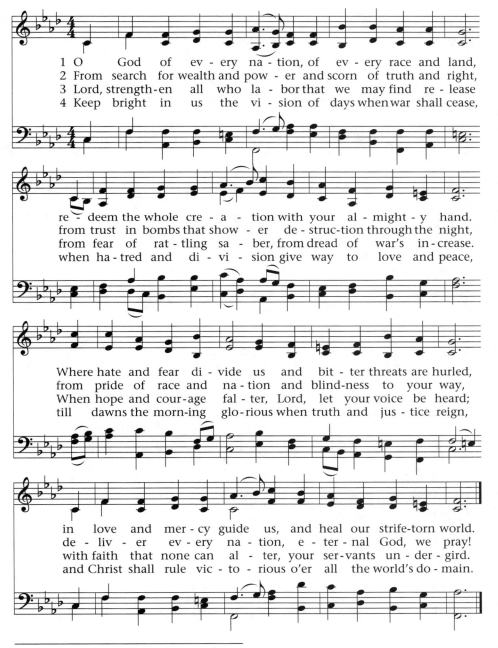

1 O God of ev-ery na-tion, of ev-ery race and land,
2 From search for wealth and pow-er and scorn of truth and right,
3 Lord, strength-en all who la-bor that we may find re-lease
4 Keep bright in us the vi-sion of days when war shall cease,

re-deem the whole cre-a-tion with your al-might-y hand.
from trust in bombs that show-er de-struc-tion through the night,
from fear of rat-tling sa-ber, from dread of war's in-crease.
when ha-tred and di-vi-sion give way to love and peace,

Where hate and fear di-vide us and bit-ter threats are hurled,
from pride of race and na-tion and blind-ness to your way,
When hope and cour-age fal-ter, Lord, let your voice be heard;
till dawns the morn-ing glo-rious when truth and jus-tice reign,

in love and mer-cy guide us, and heal our strife-torn world.
de-liv-er ev-ery na-tion, e-ter-nal God, we pray!
with faith that none can al-ter, your ser-vants un-der-gird.
and Christ shall rule vic-to-rious o'er all the world's do-main.

Words: William W. Reid, Jr. (1958) © renewed 1986 The Hymn Society
    (admin. Hope Publishing Company)
Music: Welsh, 19th c., P.D.

76 76 D

LLANGLOFFAN

This text was Reid's winning submission to a hymn search conducted by the Hymn Society in conjunction with the Fifth World Order Conference of the National Council of Churches. It is a fervent prayer for shalom through-out God's world, set to a fine traditional Welsh ballad tune that became a hymn tune in a Baptist hymnal in 1865. Try singing the 4th stanza in major!

223 For Your Gift of God the Spirit

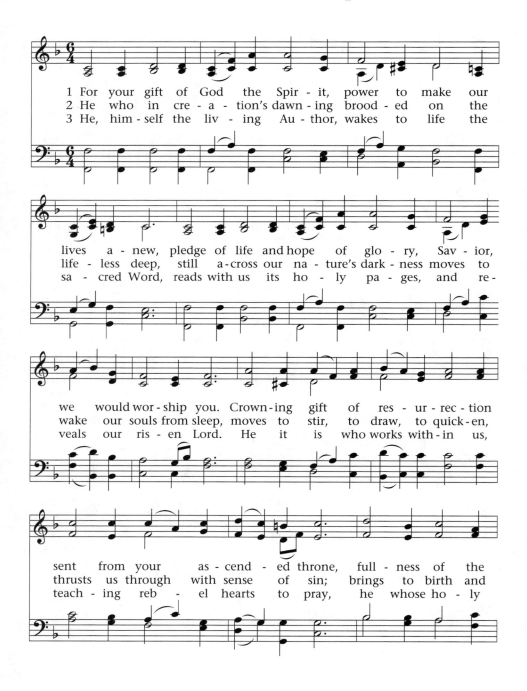

1 For your gift of God the Spir - it, power to make our
2 He who in cre - a - tion's dawn - ing brood - ed on the
3 He, him - self the liv - ing Au - thor, wakes to life the

lives a - new, pledge of life and hope of glo - ry, Sav - ior,
life - less deep, still a-cross our na - ture's dark - ness moves to
sa - cred Word, reads with us its ho - ly pa - ges, and re-

we would wor - ship you. Crown - ing gift of res - ur - rec - tion
wake our souls from sleep, moves to stir, to draw, to quick - en,
veals our ris - en Lord. He it is who works with - in us,

sent from your as - cend - ed throne, full - ness of the
thrusts us through with sense of sin; brings to birth and
teach - ing reb - el hearts to pray, he whose ho - ly

Words: Margaret Clarkson (1959) © 1960 Hope Publishing Company
Music: William P. Rowlands (1905), P.D.

87 87 D
BLAENWERN

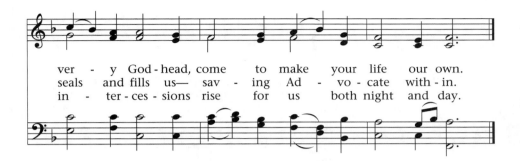

ver - y God-head, come to make your life our own.
seals and fills us— sav - ing Ad - vo - cate with - in.
in - ter - ces - sions rise for us both night and day.

4 He, the mighty God, in-dwells us;
   his to strengthen, help, empower;
   his to overcome the tempter—
   ours to call in danger's hour.
   In his strength we dare to battle
   all the raging hosts of sin,
   and by him alone we conquer
   foes without and foes within.

5 Father, grant your Holy Spirit
   in our hearts may rule today,
   grieved not, quenched not, but unhindered,
   work in us his sovereign way.
   Fill us with your holy fullness,
   God the Father, Spirit, Son;
   in us, through us, then, forever,
   shall your perfect will be done.

This is a great teaching hymn about the Holy Spirit. It's an extended hymnic pneumatology (doctrine of the Holy Spirit) originally written for InterVarsity Christian Fellowship. Blessed with a distinguished climax, BLAENWERN comes to us from the last of the Welsh revival periods.

224 Lord, Whose Love in Humble Service

1 Lord, whose love in hum-ble ser-vice bore the weight of
2 Still your chil-dren wan-der home-less; still the hun-gry
3 As we wor-ship, grant us vi-sion till your love's re-
4 Called from wor-ship in-to ser-vice, for-ward in your

hu-man need, who up-on the cross, for-sak-en, worked your
cry for bread; still the cap-tives long for free-dom; still in
veal-ing light in its height and depth and great-ness dawns up-
name we go, to the child, the youth, the a-ged, love in

mer-cy's per-fect deed, we, your ser-vants, bring the
grief we mourn our dead. As you, Lord, in deep com-
on our quick-ened sight, mak-ing known the needs and
liv-ing deeds to show. Hope and health, good-will and

wor-ship not of voice a-lone, but heart, con-se-
pas-sion healed the sick and freed the soul, use the
bur-dens your com-pas-sion bids us bear, stir-ring
com-fort, coun-sel, aid, and peace we give, that your

Words: Albert F. Bayly, 1961, alt. © 1988 Oxfort University Press
Music: Joshua Leavitt's *Christian Lyre* (1830); harm. Ralph Vaughan Williams (1906), P.D.

87 87 D
PLEADING SAVIOR

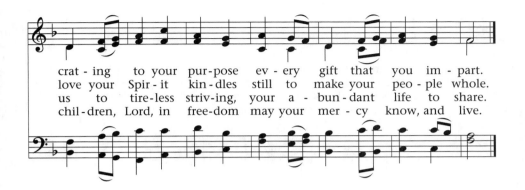

crat - ing   to your   pur-pose   ev - ery   gift that   you im - part.
love your   Spir - it   kin - dles   still to   make your   peo - ple whole.
us   to   tire-less   striv-ing,   your a - bun-dant   life to   share.
chil-dren, Lord, in   free-dom   may your   mer - cy   know, and   live.

Bayly wrote this text in response to a Hymn Society search for new hymns on Christian social service for a confer-ence on the Church and Social Welfare in 1961. PLEADING SAVIOR is a pentatonic tune that Vaughan Williams transplanted from the United States to Britain for use in his *English Hymnal* (1906).

225 Earth and All Stars

1 Earth and all stars! Come, rush - ing plan - ets!
2 Hail wind, and rain! Come, blow - ing snow - storms!
3 Trum - pet and pipes! Come, clash - ing cym - bals!
4 En - gines and steel! Come, pound - ing ham - mers!

Sing to the Lord a new song!

Oh, vic - to - ry! Or - der from cha - os!
Flow - ers and trees! Soft rus - tling dry leaves!
Harp, lute, and lyre! Low hum - ming cel - los!
Lime - stone and beams! Strong build - ing work - ers!

Sing to the Lord a new song!

Words: Herbert Brokering (1964), alt.
Music: David Johnson (1968); harm. Dale Grotenhuis (1984)
Words and Music © 1968 Augsburg Publishing House.

457 457 with refrain
EARTH AND ALL STARS

He has done mar - vel-ous things.

I too will praise him with a new song!

5 Classrooms and labs!
   Come, boiling test tubes!
   Sing to the Lord a new song!
   Athlete and band!
   Loud cheering people!
   Sing to the Lord a new song!
   Refrain

6 Knowledge and truth!
   Come, piercing wisdom!
   Sing to the Lord a new song!
   Children of God,
   dying and rising,
   Sing to the Lord a new song!
   Refrain

This is a catalogue text in which we're invited to join in singing "a new song" to the Lord along with a host of natural and cultural phenomena. Johnson wrote the energetic tune for this text, producing a hymn that suggests various options for antiphonal performance between the stanzas and the two sets of refrain lines.

226 "Forgive Our Sins As We Forgive"

1 "For - give our sins as we for - give,"
2 How can your par - don reach and bless
3 In blaz - ing light your cross re - veals
4 Lord, cleanse the depths with - in our souls

you taught us, Lord, to pray. But you a -
the un - for - giv - ing heart that broods on
the truth we dim - ly knew— what triv - ial
and bid re - sent - ment cease. Then, bound to

lone can grant us grace to live the words we say.
wrongs and will not let old bit - ter - ness de - part?
debts are owed to us, how great our debt to you.
all in bonds of love, our lives will spread your peace.

Words: Rosamond E. Herklots (1969). By permission of Oxford University Press.
Music: Scottish Psalter (1615), P.D.

86 86
DUNFERMLINE

While other hymns extol God's forgiveness of sins, this text calls us to forgive the sins of others, as Jesus sets forth in the Lord's Prayer. The rhythmic setting of this Scottish psalm tune enables singing it in two long phrases, not in four short ones (each with its own "gathering" note, which was only too common in Scottish and English psalmody).

I Come with Joy to Meet My Lord 227

1 I come with joy, a child of God, for-
2 I come with Chris - tians far and near to
3 As Christ breaks bread, and bids us share, each
4 The Spir - it of the ris - en Christ, un-

giv - en, loved, and free; the life of Je - sus
find, as all are fed, the new com - mu - ni -
proud di - vi - sion ends. The love that made us,
seen, but ev - er near, is in such friend - ship

to re - call, in love laid down for me.
ty of love in Christ's com - mu - nion bread.
makes us one, and strang - ers now are friends.
bet - ter known, a - live a - mong us here.

5 Together met, together bound
   by all that God has done,
   we'll go with joy to give the world
   the love that makes us one.

Words: Brian Wren (1970) © 1971, rev. 1995 Hope Publishing Company
Music: Appalachian folk melody (19th c.); harm. Annabel M. Buchanan (1938), P.D.

86 86
LAND OF REST

Wren helps us sing classic eucharist themes with a corporate focus: we come as forgiven sinners, Christ feeds us, though diverse we are one Christian community, and we're sent out as his representatives in the world. The tune appeared in *The Sacred Harp* (1844) before Buchanan "rediscovered" it.

228 God Sent His Son / Because He Lives

1 God sent his Son, they called him Je - sus; he came to
2 How sweet to hold a new-born ba - by, and feel the
3 And then one day I'll cross the riv - er, I'll fight life's

love, heal, and for - give. He lived and died
pride and joy it gives; but great - er still
fin - al war with pain; and then as death

to buy my par - don, an emp - ty grave is there to
the calm as - sur - ance: this child can face un - cer - tain
gives way to vic - tory, I'll see the lights of glo - ry

Refrain

prove my Sav - ior lives.
days be - cause he lives. Be-cause he lives I can face to-
and I'll know he lives.

Words: Gloria Gaither and William J. Gaither (1971)
Music: William J. Gaither (1971)

9 8 9 12 with refrain
RESURRECTION

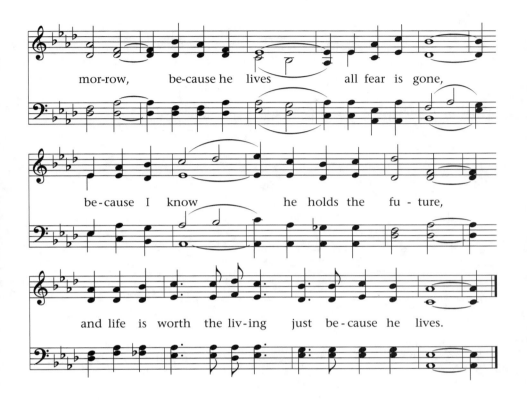

mor-row, be-cause he lives all fear is gone,

be-cause I know he holds the fu - ture,

and life is worth the liv-ing just be - cause he lives.

This song of hope was written after the birth of the Gaithers' third child. Bill and Gloria Gaither are the best modern representatives of the over 125-year-old tradition of white gospel music in the U.S.

229 Alleluia, Alleluia! Give Thanks/ Alleluia No. 1

Refrain

Al-le-lu-ia, al-le-lu-ia! Give thanks to the ris-en Lord.

Al-le-lu-ia, al-le-lu-ia! Give praise to his name.

Unison

1 Je - sus is Lord of all the earth;
2 Spread the good news o'er all the earth:
3 We have been cru - ci - fied with Christ;
4 God has pro - claimed the just re - ward:
5 Come, let us praise the liv - ing God,

he is the King of cre - a - tion.
Je - sus has died and has ris - en.
now we shall live for - ev - er.
life for his own. Al - le - lu - ia!
joy - ful - ly sing to our Sav - ior.

Words and Music: Donald Fishel (1971); harm. Dale Grotenhuis (1984)
Words and Music © 1973 International Liturgy Publications.

88 with refrain
ALLELUIA NO. 1

Fishel's Easter hymn was composed "rather spontaneously" during the summer of 1971 for his charismatic Roman Catholic parish in Ann Arbor, Michigan. This song has been widely published in modern hymnals. The opening antiphon, "Alleluia, Alleluia! Give thanks . . . ," also functions as the refrain.

When in Our Music God Is Glorified 230

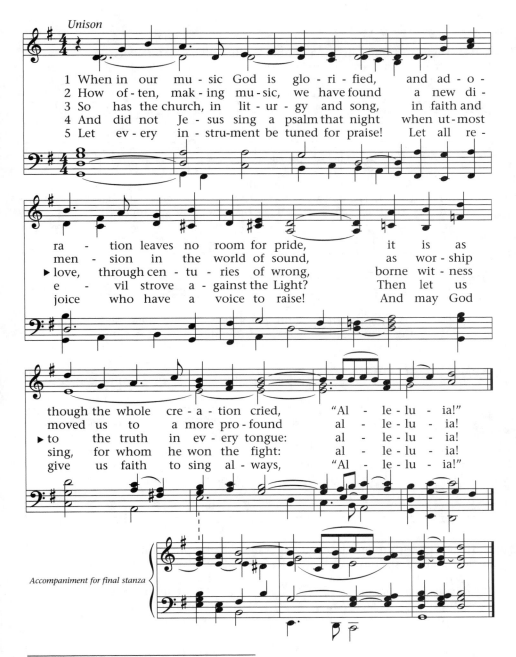

1 When in our mu-sic God is glo-ri-fied, and ad-o-ra-tion leaves no room for pride, it is as though the whole cre-a-tion cried, "Al-le-lu-ia!"

2 How of-ten, mak-ing mu-sic, we have found a new di-men-sion in the world of sound, as wor-ship moved us to a more pro-found al-le-lu-ia!

3 So has the church, in lit-ur-gy and song, in faith and love, through cen-tu-ries of wrong, borne wit-ness to the truth in ev-ery tongue: al-le-lu-ia!

4 And did not Je-sus sing a psalm that night when ut-most e-vil strove a-gainst the Light? Then let us sing, for whom he won the fight: al-le-lu-ia!

5 Let ev-ery in-stru-ment be tuned for praise! Let all re-joice who have a voice to raise! And may God give us faith to sing al-ways, "Al-le-lu-ia!"

Accompaniment for final stanza

Words: Fred Pratt Green (1971) © 1972 Hope Publishing Company
Music: Charles V. Stanford (1904), P.D.

10 10 10 4
ENGELBERG

One of the finest authors of the British "hymn explosion," Pratt Green penned these words for this tune to explain the reasons for church music while simultaneously offering "alleluias" to God. Stanford's energetic melody is designed for unison singing with no pauses between stanzas.

231 Here from All Nations

1 Here from all nations, all tongues, and all peo-ples,
2 These have come out of the great trib-u-la-tion;
3 Gone is their thirst and no more shall they hun-ger;

count-less the crowd but their voic-es are one.
now they may stand in the pres-ence of God,
God is their shel-ter, his power at their side.

Vast is the sight and ma-jes-tic their sing-ing:
serv-ing their Lord day and night in his tem-ple,
Sun shall not pain them, no burn-ing will tor-ture;

"God has the vic-tory: he reigns from the throne!"
ran-somed and cleansed by the Lamb's pre-cious blood.
Je-sus the Lamb is their shep-herd and guide.

4 He will go with them to clear living water
flowing from springs
which his mercy supplies.
Gone is their grief,
and their trials are over.
God wipes away every tear from their eyes.

5 Blessing and glory
and wisdom and power
be to the Savior again and again.
Might and thanksgiving
and honor forever
be to our God: Alleluia! Amen.

Words: Revelation 7:9-17; vers. Chrsitopher idle (1972) © 1973 The Jubilate Group
(Hope Publishing Company).
Music: *Antiphoner,* Paris (1681); harm. John B. Dykes (1868), adapt., P.D.

11 10 11 10

O QUANTA QUALIA

Idle effectively captures John's vision in Revelation 7:9-17 in words that encourage all Christians. The tune, first as-sociated with Peter Abelard's "O What Their Joy and Their Glory Must Be," comes from a French diocesan Roman Catholic chant collection. This text and music were first united in the British *Psalm Praise* (1973).

Seek Ye First the Kingdom 232

1 Seek ye first the king - dom of God and his
2 Ask and it shall be giv-en un - to you; seek and
3 We do not live by bread a - lone, but by

right - eous - ness, and all these things shall be
you shall find; knock and the door shall be
ev - ery word that pro - ceeds from the

add - ed un - to you. Al - le - lu, al - le - lu - ia.
o - pened un - to you. Al - le - lu, al - le - lu - ia.
mouth of God. Al - le - lu, al - le - lu - ia.

Words: Matthew 6:33; 7:7; 4:4; para. Karen Lafferty (1972)
Music: Karen Lafferty (1972)
Words and Music © 1972 Maranatha! Music.

irregular
LAFFERTY

A delightfully simple and memorable Bible song, this text fervently draws our attention to the words of Jesus. Lafferty recently concluded a long career as a musical missionary for Youth With a Mission. Her hymn, first published by Maranatha! Music, appears in most modern hymnals, sometimes with descant and additional anonymous stanzas.

233 There in God's Garden

1 There in God's gar-den stands the Tree of Wis-dom,
2 Its name is Je-sus, name that says, "Our Sa-vior!"
3 Thorns not its own are tan-gled in its fo-liage;
4 See how its branch-es reach to us in wel-come;

whose leaves hold forth the heal-ing of the na-tions:
There on its branch-es see the scars of suf-fering;
our greed has starved it, our des-pite has choked it.
hear what the Voice says, "Come to me, ye wear-y!

Tree of all know-ledge, Tree of all com-
see where the ten-drils of our hu-man
Yet, look! It lives! Its grief has not de-
Give me your sick-ness, give me all your

pas-sion, Tree of all beau-ty.
self-hood feed on its life-blood.
stroyed it nor fire con-sumed it.
sor-row, I will give bless-ing."

Words: Erik R. Routley (1973), based on a text by Király Imre von Pécselyi (ca. 1590-1641);
© 1976 Hinshaw Music, Inc.
Music: K. Lee Scott (1987) © 1987 MorningStar Music Publishers

11 11 11 5

SHADES MOUNTAIN

5 This is my ending, this my resurrection;
   into your hands, Lord, I commit my spirit.
   This have I searched for; now I can possess it.
   This ground is holy.

6 All heaven is singing, "Thanks to Christ whose Passion
   offers in mercy healing, strength, and pardon.
   Peoples and nations, take it, take it freely!"
   Amen! Our Savior!

Inspired by a Hungarian Good Friday poem on the tree image in Scripture, Routley's text personifies the tree of life in Revelation 22:2 as Jesus Christ, whose death and resurrection offer "healing, strength, and pardon" to all peoples. These grand words are well supported by Scott's majestic tune.

234 You Satisfy the Hungry Heart/ Gift of Finest Wheat

Refrain
Unison

You sat-is-fy the hun-gry heart with gift of fin-est wheat.

Fine

Come, give to us, O sav-ing Lord, the bread of life to eat.

1 As when a shep-herd calls his sheep, they know and heed his voice;
2 With joy-ful lips we sing to you our praise and grat - i - tude,
3 Is not the cup we bless and share the blood of Christ out-poured?

To Refrain

so when you call your fam-ily, Lord, we fol - low and re - joice.
that you should count us wor-thy, Lord, to share this heav-enly food.
Do not one cup, one loaf de - clare our one - ness in the Lord?

4 The mystery of your presence, Lord,
no mortal tongue can tell:
whom all the world cannot contain
comes in our hearts to dwell. *Refrain*

5 You give yourself to us, O Lord;
then selfless let us be
to serve each other in your name
in truth and charity. *Refrain*

Words: Omer Westendorf (1976)
Music: Robert E. Kreutz (1976)
Words and Music © 1977 Archdiocese of Philadelphia. All rights reserved.

86 86 with refrain
BICENTENNIAL

Filled with biblical images, this is one of the finest of the recent hymns for the Lord's Supper. Originally written for a Roman Catholic convention about the eucharist, Westendorf's text has been widely published in modern hymnals for use by Roman Catholics and Protestants alike. Kreutz composed the music for this text, giving us changing meters unified by melodic and rhythmic motifs.

Soon and Very Soon   235

1,4 Soon and ver-y soon, we are going to see the King!
2 No more cry-ing there— we are going to see the King!
3 No more dy-ing there— we are going to see the King!

Soon and ver-y soon, we are going to see the King!
No more cry-ing there— we are going to see the King!
No more dy-ing there— we are going to see the King!

Soon and ver-y soon, we are going to see the King!
No more cry-ing there— we are going to see the King!
No more dy-ing there— we are going to see the King!

Refrain

Hal-le-lu-jah! Hal-le-lu-jah! We're going to see the King!

Words and Music: Andraé Crouch (1976)
© 1976 Crouch Music (ASCAP) Bud John Songs (ASCAP) (adm. by
   EMI CMG Publishing).

12 12 12 with refrain
SOON AND VERY SOON

This piece by Crouch is among the finest of the more recent Black gospel hymns. Slightly syncopated and with
much textual repetition, this Advent hymn helps us confess the joys of the coming Great Day of the King, with "no
more crying, no more dying—Alleluia!"

236 Lord, You Give the Great Commission

1 Lord, you give the great com-mis-sion: "Heal the sick and
2 Lord, you call us to your ser-vice: "In my name bap-
3 Lord, you make the com-mon ho-ly: "This my bod-y,

preach the Word." Lest the church ne-glect its mis-sion
tize and teach." That the world may trust your prom-ise—
this my blood." Let us all, for earth's true glo-ry,

and the gos-pel go un-heard, help us wit-ness
life a-bun-dant meant for each— give us all new
dai-ly lift life heav-en-ward, ask-ing that the

to your pur-pose with re-newed in-teg-ri-ty;
fer-vor, draw us clos-er in com-mu-ni-ty;
world a-round us share your chil-dren's lib-er-ty;

Words: Jeffrey W. Rowthorn (1978) © 1978 Hope Publishing Company
Music: Cyril V. Taylor (1941) © 1942, renewed 1970 Hope Publishing Company

87 87 D
ABBOT'S LEIGH

Refrain

with the Spir - it's gifts em-power us for the work of min - is - try.

4 Lord, you show us love's true measure:
  "Father, what they do, forgive."
  Yet we hoard as private treasure
  all that you so freely give.
  May your care and mercy lead us
  to a just society;
  Refrain

5 Lord, you bless with words assuring:
  "I am with you to the end."
  Faith and hope and love restoring,
  may we serve as you intend,
  and, amid the cares that claim us,
  hold in mind eternity;
  Refrain

This is one of the finest modern prayer hymns about the ministries of the church. It is notable for the quotation of Christ's words in each stanza written by Rowthorn, then chaplain at Yale Divinity College. Equally distinguished, the dramatic tune comes from England; it is associated with this and other texts.

237 Tú has venido a la orilla/ You Have Come Down to the Lakeshore

Spanish 1 Tú has ve - ni - do a la o - ri - lla, no has bus -
2 Tú sa - bes bien lo que ten - go; en mi
English 1 You have come down to the lake - shore, seek - ing
2 You know full well what I have, Lord: nei - ther

ca - do ni a sa - bios ni a ri - cos;
bar - ca no hay o - ro ni es - pa - das,
nei - ther the wise nor the wealth - y,
trea - sure nor wea - pons for con - quest,

tan só - lo quie - res que yo te si - ga.
tan só - lo re - des y mi tra - ba - jo.
but on - ly ask - ing for me to fol - low.
just these my fish - nets and will for work - ing.

Estribillo/Refrain

Se - ñor, me has mi - ra - do a los o - jos,
O Lord, you have looked in - to my eyes;

Words and Music: Cesáreo Gabaraín (1976); tr. Madeleine Forell Marshall (1988)
© 1979 Cesáreo Gabaraín (admin. by OCP Publications)

8 10 10 with refrain
PESCADOR DE HOMBRES

son - ri - en - do   has   di - cho mi nom-bre;
kind - ly smil - ing,   you've called out my name.

en   la a - re - na   he de - ja - do mi bar - ca,
On   the sand   I   have a - ban-doned my small   boat;

jun - to a   ti   bus - ca - ré   o - tro mar.
now with you   I   will seek oth-er seas.

3 Tú necesitas mis manos,
  mi cansancio que a otros descanse,
  amor que quiera seguir amando.
  Estribillo

4 Tú, pescador de otros lagos,
  ansia eterna de almas
    que esperan,
  amigo bueno, que así me llamas.
  Estribillo

3 You need my hands, my exhaustion,
  working love for the rest of the weary,
  a love that's willing to go on loving.
  Refrain

4 You who have fished other waters,
  you, the longing of souls
    that are yearning:
  O loving Friend,
    you have come to call me. *Refrain*

Gabaraín, a Spanish priest involved in liturgical renewal following Vatican II, composed this hymn after a trip to Israel. Reminding us of Jesus' calling of his disciples in the stanzas, the refrain invites our similar response of following Jesus in the church's ministry today. This hymn has been translated into many languages.

238   When Jesus the Healer

Leader

1 When Je - sus the heal - er passed through Gal - i - lee,
2 A par - a - lyzed man was let down through a roof. Heal
3 The death of his daugh - ter caused Jai - rus to weep.

the deaf came to hear and the
us, heal us to - day! His sins were for - giv - en, his
The Lord took her hand, and he

blind came to see.
walk - ing the proof. Heal us, Lord Je - sus!
raised her from sleep.

4 When blind Bartimaeus
   cried out to the Lord,
Heal us, heal us today!
his faith made him whole
   and his sight was restored.
Heal us, Lord Jesus!

5 The lepers were healed
   and the demons cast out.
Heal us, heal us today!
A bent woman straightened
   to laugh and to shout.
Heal us, Lord Jesus!

6 The twelve were commissioned
   and sent out in twos
Heal us, heal us today!
to make the sick whole
   and to spread the good news.
Heal us, Lord Jesus!

7 There's still so much sickness
   and suffering today.
Heal us, heal us today!
We gather together
   for healing and pray:
Heal us, Lord Jesus!

Words and Music: Peter D. Smith (1978) © 1978 Stainer & Bell, Ltd. and Methodist Church (UK)   11 6 11 5
Division of Education and Youth (Admin. Hope Publishing Company   HEALER

This hymn focuses on the healing miracles of Jesus, complementing other hymns that focus on the parables of Jesus (e.g. #245). Written in a call-and-response format during a workshop at Iona in 1975, this song comes from a British Methodist minister and folksinger.

Baptized in Water 239

Unison

1 Bap-tized in wa - ter, sealed by the Spir - it, cleansed by the
2 Bap-tized in wa - ter, sealed by the Spir - it, dead in the
3 Bap-tized in wa - ter, sealed by the Spir - it, marked with the

blood of Christ, our King; heirs of sal - va - tion,
tomb with Christ, our King; one with his ris - ing,
sign of Christ, our King; born of one Fa - ther,

trust-ing his prom - ise, faith - ful-ly now God's praise we sing.
freed and for - giv - en, thank - ful-ly now God's praise we sing.
we are his chil - dren, joy - ful-ly now God's praise we sing.

Words: Michael Saward (1981) © 1982 The Jubilate Group (Admin. Hope Publishing Co., Carol
    Stream, IL 60188). All rights reserved. Used by permission.
Music: Scottish, *Songs and Hymns of the Gael* (1888); harm. Dale Grotenhuis (1985)
    © 1987 Faith Alive Christian Resources

558 D

BUNESSAN

This gem of a hymn is a classic example of "small is beautiful." Here we sing a compact theology of Christian
baptism to a memorable folk tune, which many associate with the popular setting of Eleanor Farjeon's "Morning
Has Broken."

240   O God Beyond All Praising

1 O   God be-yond all prais-ing, we wor-ship you to - day
2 Then hear, O gra-cious Sav - ior, ac - cept the love we   bring,

and   sing   the love a - maz - ing that songs can-not re - pay;
that   we   who know your fa - vor may   serve you as   our King;

for   we   can on - ly won - der at   ev - ery gift you send,
and wheth - er our to - mor-rows be   filled with good or   ill,

at   bless - ings   with - out num-ber and   mer-cies with - out end.
we'll tri - umph through our sor-rows and   rise to bless you still:

Words: Michael Perry (1982) © 1982 The Jubilate Group (admin. by Hope Publishing Company)   13 13 13 13 13 13
Music: Gustav T. Holst (1918), P.D.   THAXTED

We lift our hearts be - fore you and wait up-on your Word,
to mar - vel at your beau - ty and glo-ry in your ways,

we hon - or and a-dore you, our great and might - y Lord.
and make a joy - ful du - ty our sac - ri - fice of praise.

A grand hymn of worship, Perry's text was published in *Hymns for Today's Church* (1982), one of the Jubilate publications that he edited. In 1921 Holst extracted his THAXTED music from the "Jupiter" movement of his astrological orchestral suite, *The Planets*, Op. 32; it has been associated as a glorious ABA hymn tune with this and other texts.

241 O Lord, Hear My Prayer

1 O Lord, hear my prayer, O Lord, hear my prayer:
2 The Lord is my song, the Lord is my praise:

when I call an-swer me. O Lord, hear my prayer, O
All my hope comes from God. The Lord is my song, the

Lord, hear my prayer: come and lis-ten to me.
Lord is my praise: God, the well-spring of life.

Words: Psalm 102:1-2; adapt. The Community of Taizé
Music: Jacques Berthier (1982)
© 1991 Les Presses de Taizé (France) (admin. by GIA Publications, Inc.)

556D
HEAR MY PRAYER

This is one of the best-known and most commonly used prayer choruses from the Taizé Community in France. In the Taizé tradition it would be sung repeatedly, each time with alternate instrumentation for accompaniment. It can also be sung as a frame around prayers or as part of a litany. Sing stanza 1 with prayers of petition and stanza 2 with prayers of thanksgiving.

Go, My Children, with My Blessing 242

1 Go, my chil-dren, with my bless-ing, nev - er a - lone.
2 Go, my chil-dren, sins for - giv - en, at peace and pure.
3 Go, my chil-dren, fed and nour-ished, clos - er to me.
4 I, the Lord, will bless and keep you, and give you peace.

Wak - ing, sleep-ing, I am with you, you are my own.
Here you learned how much I love you, what I can cure.
Grow in love and love by serv-ing, joy - ful and free.
I, the Lord, will smile up-on you, and give you peace.

In my love's bap-tis-mal riv-er, I have made you mine for-
Here you heard my dear Son's sto-ry, here you touched him, saw his
Here my Spir-it's pow-er filled you, here his ten - der com-fort
I, the Lord, will be your Fa-ther, Sav-ior, Com-fort-er, and

ev - er. Go, my chil-dren, with my bless-ing, you are my own.
glo - ry. Go, my chil-dren, sins for - giv - en, at peace and pure.
stilled you. Go, my chil-dren, fed and nour-ished, joy - ful and free.
Broth - er. Go, my chil-dren. I will keep you, and give you peace.

Words: Jaroslav J. Vajda (1983) © 1983 Concordia Publishing House
Music: trad. Welsh melody, *Musical Relicks of the Welsh Bards* (1784);
    harm. Ralph Vaughen Williams (1906), alt., P.D.

84 84 88 84
AR HYD Y NOS

A Lutheran pastor in English and Slovak-speaking congregations in the U.S., Vajda wrote this text for the
traditional Welsh tune. The text is an expansion of the Aaronic Blessing (Num. 6:24-26), but is unusual because
it is God's voice that is sung by the congregation to each other.

243 Blest Are They

1 Blest are they, the poor in spir - it; theirs is the
2 Blest are they, the low - ly ones; they shall in -
3 Blest are they____ who show mer - cy; mer - cy

king - dom of God. Blest are they,
her - it the earth. Blest are they who
shall be theirs. Blest are they, the

full of sor - row; they shall be con - soled.
hun - ger and thirst; they shall have their fill.
pure of heart; they shall see God.

Words and music: David Haas (1985) based on Matthew 5:3-12, © 1986 GIA Publications, Inc.

irregular
BLEST ARE THEY

Refrain

Re - joice and be glad!

Bless-ed are you; ho - ly are you. Re - joice

and be glad! Yours is the king-dom of

Final Ending

God.

4 Blest are they who seek peace;
  they are the children of God.
  Blest are they who suffer in faith;
  the glory of God is theirs.

5 Blest are you who suffer hate,
  all because of me.
  Rejoice and be glad, yours is the kingdom;
  shine for all to see.

This is one of the most notable settings of Jesus' beatitudes in Matthew 5, made even more memorable by the rousing refrain. Haas is an important figure in the post-Vatican II developments of Roman Catholic church music.

244 Christ, Who Is in the Form of God

Unison

1 Christ, who is in the form of God, did not re-
tain his loft-y place, but, tak-ing on a ser-vant's
role, be-came a mem-ber of our race. And be-ing found in hu-man
form, hum-bly he suf-fered fur-ther loss by will-ing-
ly ac-cept-ing death— yes, ev-en death up-on a cross.

2 There-fore has God ex-alt-ed him and raised him
to the high-est place and giv-en him that match-less
name, wor-thy of all names to be praised; that at the name of Je-sus
Christ should ev-ery crea-ture bend the knee, and ev-ery
tongue con-fess him Lord, to God's own glo-ry end-less-ly.

Words: Philippians 2:6–11; vers. David T. Koyzis (1985) © 1985 David T. Koyzis
Music: C. Hubert H. Parry (1916); arr. Janet Wyatt (1977) © 1916, 1944, 1977 Roberton Publications.
Reprinted by permission of the publisher, Goodmusic Publishing Ltd.

88 88 D
JERUSALEM

Many scholars think Paul is quoting an early Christian baptism creed in this well-known text from his epistle to
the Philippians. Parry's tune, with its fine climax, is a majestic fit for this profound confession of faith.

You Are Salt for the Earth/ 245
Bring Forth the Kingdom

Unison

1 You are salt for the earth, O peo-ple: salt for the king-dom of God!
2 You are a light on a hill, O peo-ple: light for the cit - y of God!
3 You are a seed of the Word, O peo-ple: live for the king-dom of God!

Share the fla-vor of life, O peo-ple: life in the king-dom of God!
Shine so ho - ly and bright, O peo-ple: shine for the king-dom of God!
Seeds of mer-cy and seeds of jus-tice, grow in the king-dom of God!

Refrain

Bring forth the king-dom of mer-cy; pray for the king-dom of peace;

work for the king-dom of jus-tice; hope for the cit-y of God!

Words and Music: Marty Haugen (1986), based on Matthew 5:13-16, 13:18-23
© 1986 GIA Publications, Inc.

irregular
Haugen

Written originally for a catechism conference, this text challenges us with the biblical images of salt, light, and
seed; the call for our commitment is propelled by strong verbs: share, shine, bring forth, pray, work, and hope.
Haugen's vigorous music invites antiphonal performance: try the stanzas with a soloist or choir, and the full
congregation on the refrain.

246 Wash, O God, Our Sons and Daughters

1 Wash, O God, our sons and daugh-ters, where your cleans-ing wa-ters flow.

Num-ber them a - mong your peo-ple; bless as Christ blessed long a - go.

Weave them gar-ments bright and spark-ling; com-pass them with love and light.

Fill, a-noint them; send your Spir - it, ho-ly dove and heart's de-light.

2 We who bring them long for nurture;
by your milk may we be fed.
Let us join your feast, partaking
cup of blessing, living bread.
God, renew us, guide our footsteps,
free from sin and all its snares,
one with Christ in living, dying,
by your Spirit, children, heirs.

3 Oh, how deep your holy wisdom!
Unimagined, all your ways!
To your name be glory, honor!
With our lives we worship, praise!
We your people stand before you,
water-washed and Spirit-born.
By your grace, our lives we offer.
Recreate us; God, transform!

Words: Ruth Duck (1987) © 1989 The United Methodist Publishing House   87 87 D
    (admin. by The Copyright Company)
Music: *The Sacred Harp* (1844); arr. Selected Hymns (1985) © 1985 Augsburg Fortress   BEACH SPRING

Filled with biblical quotations and allusions, Duck's baptism text was commissioned for the United Methodist
Hymnal (1989). The strong pentatonic tune is attributed to Benjamin F. White, a co-editor of *The Sacred Harp*, one of
the most important shape-note hymnals in American history.

As We Gather at Your Table   247

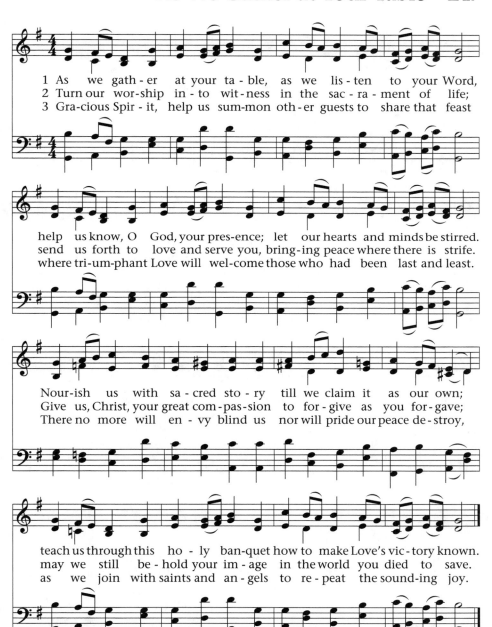

1 As   we gath-er   at your ta-ble,   as   we   lis-ten   to   your Word,
2 Turn our wor-ship in-to wit-ness in the sac-ra-ment of   life;
3 Gra-cious Spir-it, help us sum-mon oth-er guests to   share that feast

help   us know, O   God, your pres-ence;   let   our hearts and minds be stirred.
send   us forth to   love and serve you,   bring-ing peace where there is   strife.
where tri-um-phant Love will   wel-come those who had   been   last and least.

Nour-ish   us   with   sa-cred sto-ry   till we claim it   as   our own;
Give   us, Christ, your great com-pas-sion   to   for-give as   you for-gave;
There no more will   en-vy blind us   nor will pride our peace de-stroy,

teach us through this   ho-ly ban-quet how to make Love's vic-tory known.
may we   still   be-hold your im-age   in the world you died   to   save.
as   we   join   with saints and an-gels   to re-peat   the sound-ing joy.

Words: Carl P. Daw, Jr. (1989) © 1989 Hope Publishing Co.   87 87 D
Music: *Oude en Nieuwe Hollantse Boerenlietjes en Contradansen* (1710); arr. Julius Röntgen (1855-1932) IN BABILONE
    and Ralph Vaughan Williams (1906)

In this Lord's Supper text, Daw sets out strong convictions about the sacramentality of the eucharist, preaching, and all of life. IN BABILONE is an older Dutch dance tune that Ralph Vaughan Williams turned into a sturdy hymn tune for the *English Hymnal* (1906) from an arrangement by Röntgen.

248 You, Lord, Are Both Lamb and Shepherd

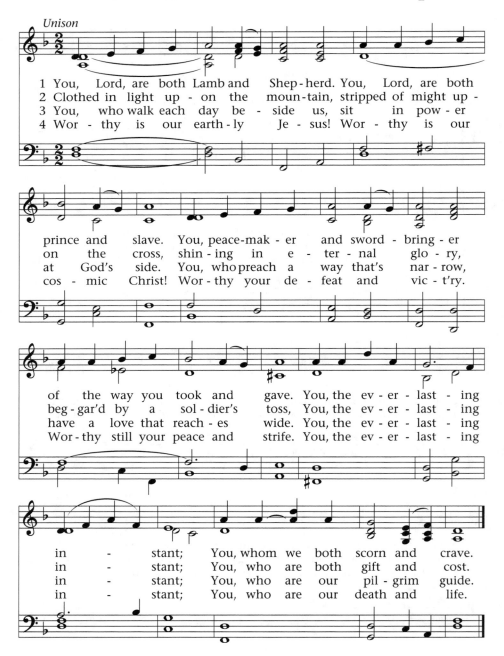

1 You, Lord, are both Lamb and Shep-herd. You, Lord, are both
2 Clothed in light up-on the moun-tain, stripped of might up-
3 You, who walk each day be-side us, sit in pow-er
4 Wor-thy is our earth-ly Je-sus! Wor-thy is our

prince and slave. You, peace-mak-er and sword-bring-er
on the cross, shin-ing in e-ter-nal glo-ry,
at God's side. You, who preach a way that's nar-row,
cos-mic Christ! Wor-thy your de-feat and vic-t'ry.

of the way you took and gave. You, the ev-er-last-ing
beg-gar'd by a sol-dier's toss, You, the ev-er-last-ing
have a love that reach-es wide. You, the ev-er-last-ing
Wor-thy still your peace and strife. You, the ev-er-last-ing

in - stant; You, whom we both scorn and crave.
in - stant; You, who are both gift and cost.
in - stant; You, who are our pil-grim guide.
in - stant; You, who are our death and life.

Words: Sylvia Dunstan (1991) © 1991 GIA Publications, Inc.
Music: French (17th c.) *Chansons Populaires de Provinces de France* (1860), P.D.

87 87 87
PICARDY

This thoughtful Christological text by one of Canada's most prominent hymn authors thrives on paradox, a device little used in hymnody because the singing tempos of most congregational songs leave little time to ponder the nuances of each paradox relationship. Note the fitting musical paradox of the melisma (several tones on one syllable) on the word "instant."

For the Music of Creation   249

1 For   the mu-sic of cre-a-tion, for the song your Spir-it sings,
2 Psalms and sym-pho-nies ex-alt you, drum and trum-pet, string and reed,
3 All   the voic-es of the a-ges in tran-scen-dent cho-rus meet,

for your sound's di-vine ex-pres-sion, burst of joy in liv-ing things:
sim-ple   mel-o-dies ac-claim you, tunes that rise from deep-est need,
wor-ship   lift-ing up the sens-es, hands that praise, and danc-ing feet;

God,   our God, the world's com-pos-er, hear us,   ech-oes of your voice;
hymns of long-ing and be-long-ing, car-ols from a cheer-ful throat,
o - ver dis-cord and di-vi-sion mu-sic speaks your joy and peace,

mu-sic is your art, your glo-ry; let the hu-man heart re-joice!
lilt of lul-la-by and love song catch-ing heav-en in a note.
har-mo-ny of earth and heav-en, song of God that can-not cease!

Words: Shirley Erena Murray (1992) © 1992 Hope Publishing Company
Music: *Gross Catholisch Gesangbuch*, Nüremberg (1631), P.D.

87 87 D
OMNIE DIE

Murray, who hails from New Zealand, is a fine author of hymn texts that often present fresh images, as in this hymn in which God is pictured as the composer of creation who then inspires our songs to worship him. The tune, from a Roman Catholic hymnal, was made popular by Ralph Vaughan Williams in the *English Hymnal* (1906).

250 For All the Faithful Women

1 For all the faith-ful wom-en who served in days of old,
2 *Insert appropriate stanza(s).*
3 O God, for saints and ser-vants, those named and those un-known,
4 All praise to God the Fa-ther! All praise to Christ the Son!

to you shall thanks be giv-en; to all, their sto-ry told.
in whom through all the a-ges your light of glo-ry shone,
All praise the Ho-ly Spir-it, who binds the Church in one!

They served with strength and glad-ness in tasks your wis-dom gave.
we of-fer glad thanks-giv-ing and fer-vent prayer we raise
With saints who went be-fore us, with saints who wit-ness still,

To you their lives bore wit-ness, pro-claimed your power to save.
that, faith-ful in your ser-vice, our lives may sing your praise.
we sing glad al-le-lu-ias and strive to do your will.

Words: Herman G. Stuempfle (1993), alt. © 1993, 1997, 2003 GIA Publications, Inc.
Music: Finish (19th c.); harm. Joseph Herl (1993); harm. © 1998 Concordia Publishing House

76 76 D
NYLAND

Miriam

5 We praise your name for Miriam,
who sang triumphantly
while Pharaoh's vaunted army
lay drowned beneath the sea.
As Israel marched to freedom,
her chains of bondage gone,
so may we reach the kingdom
your mighty arm has won.
Exodus 15:19-21

Hannah

6 To Hannah, praying childless
before your throne of grace,
you gave a son and called him
to serve before your face.
Grant us her perseverance;
Lord, teach us how to pray
and trust in your deliverance
when darkness hides our way.
1 Samuel 1:1—2:10

Ruth

7 For Ruth, who left her homeland
and ventured forth in faith,
who pledged to serve and worship
Naomi's God till death,
we praise you, God of Israel,
and pray for hearts set free
to bind ourselves to others
in love and loyalty.
Ruth 1:8-18

Mary, Mother of Our Lord

8 We sing of Mary, mother,
fair maiden, full of grace.
She bore the Christ, our brother,
who came to save our race.
May we, with her, surrender
ourselves to your command
and lay upon your altar
our gifts of heart and hand.
Luke 1:26-38

Martha and Mary

9 We sing of busy Martha,
who toiled with pot and pan
while Mary sat in silence
to hear the Word again.
Christ, keep our hearts attentive
to truth that you declare,
and strengthen us for service
when work becomes our prayer.
Luke 10:38-42

The Woman at the Well

10 Recall the outcast woman
with whom the Lord conversed;
Christ gave her living water
to quench her deepest thirst.
Like hers, our hearts are yearning;
Christ offers us his Word.
Then may our lips be burning
to witness to our Lord.
John 4:1-42

Mary Magdalene

11 We sing your praise for Mary,
who came at Easter dawn
to look for Jesus' body
and found her Lord was gone.
But, as with joy she saw him
in resurrection light,
may we by faith behold him,
the Day who ends our night!
John 20:1-18

Dorcas

12 Lord, hear our thanks for Dorcas,
who served the sick and poor.
Her hands were cups of kindness,
her heart an open door.
Send us, O Christ, your Body,
where people cry in pain,
and touch them with compassion
to make them whole again.
Acts 9:36

Eunice and Lois

13 For Eunice and for Lois we sing our thanks and praise.
Young Timothy they nurtured and led him in your ways.
Raise up in every household true teachers of your Word
whose lives will bear clear witness to Christ, our risen Lord.
2 Timothy 1:5

Along with the heroes of faith mentioned in Hebrews 11, this hymn honors a number of women from biblical history who are part of the "great cloud of witnesses" of the Christian tradition. The text, with its choice of stanzas, was penned by a Lutheran pastor and professor of preaching as a sermon hymn; the folk tune is also known as KUORTANE.

251 View the Present Through the Promise

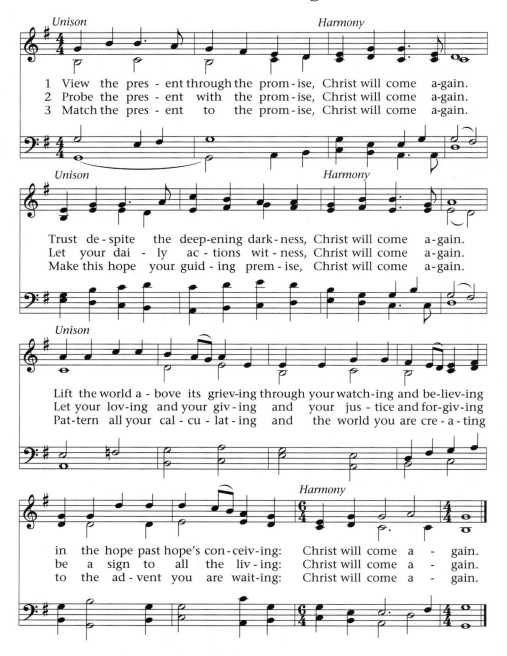

Words: Thomas H. Troeger (1994) © 1994 Oxford University Press, Inc.
Music: Roy Hopp (1997) © 1997 Roy Hopp

85 85 88 85
FRANKLIN PARK

This is a fine Advent text by Troeger, a professor of preaching. Contrary to the speculative millennial discussions among some Christians, in these words we sing the profound and yet simple confession "Christ will come again" (in harmony) in the midst of the joys and sorrows (in unison) of our everyday lives.

God Has Gone Up with Shouts of Joy! 252

1 God has gone up with shouts of joy! Christ claims the throne of glo - ry: im - mor - tal Word in mor - tal flesh to share with God our sto - ry of hu - mans lost to death and sin who ache to be in - vit-ed in to Love's e - ter - nal bless - ing.

2 Christ has gone up,
   still bearing wounds,
   still bound to race and gender;
   his royal robe all crimson blood;
   his triumph all surrender.
   Now we, though bound
     to who we are,
   can follow, with our pain and scars,
   to Love's eternal blessing.

3 Christ has gone up!
   Now Christ in us
   leads all the world to glory.
   The Word finds voice on Fiery Breath;
   our lives relate the story
   of how God went
     through death and hell
   that we might have Emmanuel
   and Love's eternal blessing.

Words: James Hart Brumm (1994) © 2001, Wayne Leupold Editions, Inc. 87 87 887
Music: Bohemian Brethren's *Kirchengesänge* (1556); harm. Heinrich Riemann (1895), P.D. MIT FREUDEN ZART

James Hart Brumm is a pastor in the Reformed Church in America and hymn text writer. This hymn is a joyous celebration of Christ's ascension and the call to ministry that arises out of it for all of us. It moves from how Christ shares our story with God to how we share Christ's story with the world. This text follows the three points of the answer to Question 45 of the Heidelberg Catechism ("How does Christ's ascension benefit us?"). This music is also used with "Sing Praise to God Who Reigns Above" (66).

253 Siyahamba/
We Are Marching in the Light of God

Zulu Si - ya-hamb' e - ku-kha-nyen' kwen-khos', si - ya-
English We are march - ing* in the light of God, we are
Spanish Ca - mi - nan - do en la luz de Dios, ca - mi -

nyen' kwen khos'.
light of God.
luz de Dios

hamb' e - ku - kha - nyen' kwen - khos'. nyen' kwen kha-
march-ing in the light of God. light of, the
nan - do en la luz de Dios. luz de, la

(khos') Si - ya - ham - ba_____
(God) We are march-ing_____
(Dios) Ca - mi - nan - do_____

nyen' kwen-khos'. Si - ya - ham - ba, ham - ba, si - ya -
light of God. We are march-ing, march-ing, we are
luz de Dios. Ca - mi - nan - do va - mos, ca - mi -

alternate text: dancing, praying, singing

Words and Music: South African (20th c.); tr. *Freedom Is Coming* (1984)
© 1984 Utryck (admin. by Walton Music Corp.)

irregular
SIYAHAMBA

This is a South African freedom song, originally in Zulu, that arose during the infamous Apartheid era. Sing this in the various languages given, or with the additional suggested verbs. In the Zulu choral tradition this would be sung in harmony, with perhaps only a hand drum such as a djembe for accompaniment.

254 In Christ Alone

1 In Christ a-lone my hope is found; he is my
2 In Christ a-lone, who took on flesh— full-ness of
3 There in the ground his bod-y lay, light of the
4 No guilt in life, no fear in death, this is the

light, my strength, my song— this cor-ner-stone, this sol-id
God in help-less babe— this gift of love and right-eous-
world by dark-ness slain; then, burst-ing forth in glo-rious
power of Christ in me; from life's first cry to fi-nal

ground, firm through the fierc-est drought and storm.
ness, scorned by the ones he came to save.
day, up from the grave he rose a-gain!
breath, Je-sus com-mands my des-ti-ny.

What heights of love, what depths of peace, when fears are
'Til on the cross as Je-sus died, the wrath of
And as he stands in vic-to-ry, sin's curse has
No power of hell, no hu-man plan, can ev-er

Words and Music: Keith Getty and Stuart Townend (2002)
© 2002 Thankyou Music (PRS) (admin. worldwide by EMI CMG Publishing
excluding Europe which is admin. by Kingswaysongs.com).

88 88 D
IN CHRIST ALONE

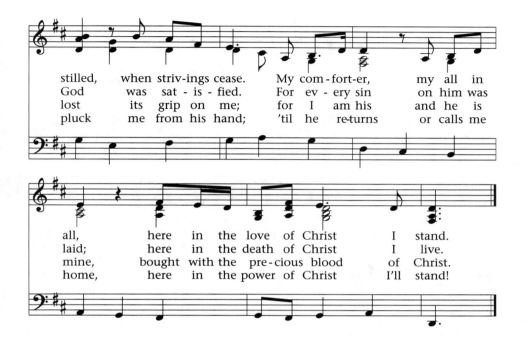

stilled, when striv-ings cease. My com-fort-er, my all in
God was sat - is - fied. For ev - ery sin on him was
lost its grip on me; for I am his and he is
pluck me from his hand; 'til he re-turns or calls me

all, here in the love of Christ I stand.
laid; here in the death of Christ I live.
mine, bought with the pre-cious blood of Christ.
home, here in the power of Christ I'll stand!

Combining Pauline Christology ("In Christ…") with narrative allusions to the life of Christ, and provided with a classically-shaped AABA tune, this hymn is one of the most-loved, most profound, and most congregationally-suitable of all the songs from the contemporary Praise & Worship movement.

255   When Memory Fades

1 When mem-ory fades, and rec-og-ni-tion fal-ters,
2 As frail-ness grows, and youth-ful strengths di-min-ish,
3 With-in your Spir-it, good-ness lives un-fad-ing.

when eyes we love grow dim, and minds con-fused, speak to our
in wea-ry arms which worked their ear-nest fill, your ag-ing
The past and fu-ture min-gle in-to one. All joys re-

souls of love that nev-er al-ters; speak to our hearts, by
ser-vants la-bor now to fin-ish their earth-ly tasks, as
main, un-shad-owed light per-vad-ing. No val-ued deed will

pain and fear a-bused. O God of life and heal-ing peace, em-
fits your mer-cy's will. We grieve their wan-ing, yet re-joice, be-
ev-er be un-done. Your mind en-folds all fi-nite acts and

Words: Mary Louise Bringle (2002) © 2002 GIA Publications, Inc.
Music: Jean Sibelius (1900) © Breitkopf & Härtel

11 10 11 10 11 10
FINLANDIA

power us   with pa - tient cour - age, by your grace   in - fused.
liev - ing,   your arms, un - wea - ried, shall up - hold   us still.
of - ferings.   Held   in your heart, our death-less life   is won.

Bringle's text recognizes our aging population—a new theme in contemporary hymnody. Seniors are part of Christ's body everywhere and join in the song of the church even when their abilities diminish. For FINLANDIA, see "Be Still, My Soul" (103).

256 God, We Sing Your Glorious Praises

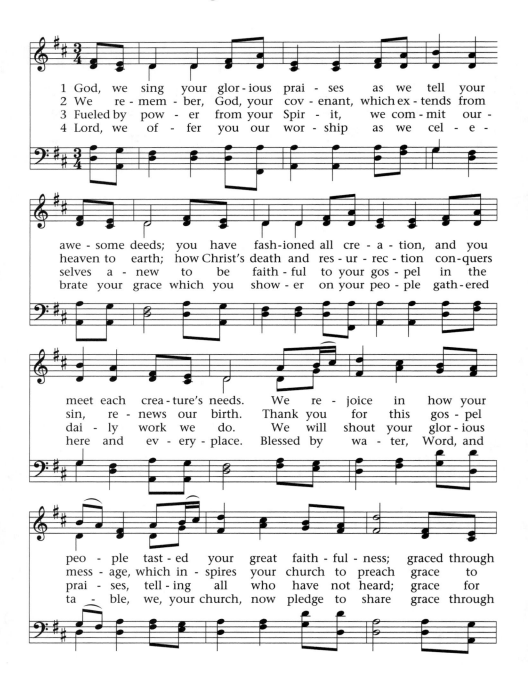

1 God, we sing your glor - ious prai - ses as we tell your
2 We re - mem - ber, God, your cov - enant, which ex - tends from
3 Fueled by pow - er from your Spir - it, we com - mit our -
4 Lord, we of - fer you our wor - ship as we cel - e -

awe - some deeds; you have fash-ioned all cre - a - tion, and you
heaven to earth; how Christ's death and res - ur - rec - tion con-quers
selves a - new to be faith - ful to your gos - pel in the
brate your grace which you show - er on your peo - ple gath - ered

meet each crea - ture's needs. We re - joice in how your
sin, re - news our birth. Thank you for this gos - pel
dai - ly work we do. We will shout your glor - ious
here and ev - ery - place. Blessed by wa - ter, Word, and

peo - ple tast - ed your great faith - ful - ness; graced through
mess - age, which in - spires your church to preach grace to
prai - ses, tell - ing all who have not heard; grace for
ta - ble, we, your church, now pledge to share grace through

Words: Bert Polman (2006) © 2006 Faith Alive Christian Resources
Music: John Wyeth's *Repository of Sacred Music, Part II* (1813), P.D.

87 87 D
NETTLETON

ev - ery gen-er - a - tion, we your might - y acts pro - fess.
ev - ery gen-er - a - tion in our deeds and in our speech.
ev - ery gen-er - a - tion is em - bo - died in your Word.
ev - ery gen-er - a - tion in our wit - ness, work, and prayer.

Written by an editor of this volume, this text was chosen as the first-place winner in a hymn search for the 150th anniversary of the Christian Reformed Church in 2007, and then united with NETTLETON, a lively melody from Wyeth's camp meeting songbook.

Copyright Holders

Each song under copyright, whether text, tune, or arrangement, is indicated as such at the bottom of the first page of each song. If you wish to reproduce (or reprint) any copyrighted words or music contained in this book, please contact the copyright holder for permission or use an approved license.

Abingdon Press
See Copyright Company, The

Alfred Publishing
PO Box 10003
Van Nuys, CA 91410-0003
Phone: 818-891-599
Fax: 818-871-2369
www.alfred.com

Archdiocese of Philadelphia
222 North 17th Street
Philadelphia, PA 19103-1299
Phone: 215-587-3500
Fax: 215-587-3561

Augsburg Fortress
100 South Fifth Street, PO Box 1209
Minneapolis, MN 55440-1209
Phone: 612-330-3300
Fax: 612-330-3455
copyright@augsburgfortress.org

Belwin-Mills Publishing Corpration
See Alfred Publishing

Breitkopf & Hartel
Walkmühlstraße 52
D-65195 Wiesbaden
Deutschland/Germany
Phone: 0611 45008-0
Fax: 0611 45008 59/60/61
info@breitkopf.com
www.breitkopf.com

Chappell & Company, Incorporated
See Alfred Publishing

Church Pension Fund, The
See Church Publishing Incorporated

Church Publishing Incorporated
445 Fifth Ave
New York, NY 10016
Phone: 800-242-1918

Concordia Publishing House
3558 South Jefferson Street
St. Louis, MO 63118-3968
Phone: 314-268-1000
www.cph.org

Copyright Company, The
PO Box 128139
Nashville, TN 37212-8139
Phone: 615-244-9848
Fax: 615-244-9850
www.thecopyrightco.com

E.C. Schirmer Music Company,
a division of ECS Publishing
138 Ipswich Street
Boston, MA 02215
Phone 617-236-1935
Fax 617-236-0261
office@ecspub.com
www.ecspub.com

EMI CMG Publishing
PO Box 5085
Brentwood, TN 37024
Phone: 615-371-4216
Fax: 615-371-6897
www.emicmgpublishing.com

Faith Alive Christian Resources
2850 Kalamazoo Avenue SE
Grand Rapids, MI 49560
Phone: 800-333-8300
Fax: 616-726-1164
permissions@FaithAliveResources.org

Gaither Copyright Management
1703 South Park Avenue
Alexandria, IN 46001
Phone: 765-724-8233

GIA Publications, Incorporated
7404 South Mason Avenue
Chicago, IL 60638
Phone: 708-496-3858
Fax: 708-496-3828
www.giamusic.com

GoodMusic Publishing, Limited
GOODMUSIC Company
PO Box 100, Tewkesbury GL20 7YQ
United Kingdom
Phone: 01684 773883
Fax: 01684 773884
sales@goodmusicpublishing.co.uk
www.goodmusicpublishing.co.uk

Grant, John W. (the estate of)
Apt. 1002
86 Gloucester Street
Toronto, ON M4Y 2S2
Canada

Hinshaw Music, Incorporated
PO Box 470
Chapel Hill, NC 27514-0470
Phone: 919-933-1691
Fax: 919-967-3399

Hope Publishing Company
380 South Main Place
Carol Stream, IL 60188
Phone: 800-323-1049
Fax: 630-665-2552
www.hopepublishing.com

Hopp, Roy
1676 Ridgemoor SE
Grand Rapids, MI 49506

International Liturgy Publications
PO Box 50476
Nashville, TN 37205
Phone: 888-898-7664
www.ILPmusic.org

Koyzis, David T.
Redeemer University College 219E
777 Garner Road East
Ancaster, ON L9K 1J4
Canada
Phone: 905-648-2131
Fax: 905-648-2134

JASRAC
3-6-12 Vehara
Shibuya-ku
Tokyo 151-8540
Japan
Phone: +81-3-3481-2144
Fax: +81-3-3481-2154
kouhou@nri.co.jp

Manna Music, Incorporated
PO Box 218
Pacific City, OR 97135
Phone: 503-965-6112
Fax: 503-965-6880
pcmannamusic@oregoncoast.com

Maranatha Music, Incorporated
See Music Services

MCS America, Incorporated
1301 16th Avenue South
Nashville, TN 37212-2923
Phone: 615-250-4600
Fax: 615-240-4699
info@mcsamerica.net

Morningstar Music Publishers
1727 Larkin Williams Road
Fenton, MO 63026-2024
Phone: 800-647-2117
Fax: 636-308-0121
www.morningstarmusic.com

Music Services
5409 Maryland Way, Suite 200
Brentwood, TN 37027
Phone: 615-371-1320
Fax: 615-371-1351
licensing@musicservices.org
www.musicservices.org

Novello & Company, Limited
See Shawnee Press, Incorporated

OCP Publications
5536 NE Hassalo
Portland, OR 97213
Phone: 800-548-8749

Oxford University Press
Music Department
Great Clarendon Street
Oxford OX2 6DP
United Kingdom
Phone: +44 (0) 1865 556767
Fax: +44 (0) 1865 355060
www.oup.com/uk/music

Presbyterian Publishing Corporation
100 Witherspoon St
Louisville, KY 40202-1396
Phone: 502-569-8308
Fax: 800-541-5113

Seerveld, Calvin
Toronto Tuppence Press
332 Senlac Rd
Toronto, ON M2R 1R3
Canada
ttp@icscanada.edu

Selah Publishing Company
4055 Cloverleaf Street
PO Box 98066
Pittsburgh, PA 15227
Phone: 412-886-1020
Fax: 412-886-1022
www.selahpub.com

Shawnee Press, Incorporated
1107 – 17th Ave South
Nashville, TN 37212
Phone: 615-320-5300
Fax: 615-320-7306
info@shawneepress.com

Stainer & Bell, Limited
See Hope Publishing Company

United Methodist Publishing House
See Copyright Company, The

United Reformed Church
86 Tavistock Place
London WC1H 9RT
United Kingdom

Walton Music Corporation
1909 White Plains Road
Chapel Hill, NC 27514
Phone: 919-929-1330

Warner/Chapell Music, Incorporated
See Word Music Group, LLC

Warner-Tamerlane
See Alfred Publishing

Wayne Leupold Editions, Incorporated
8510 Triad Drive
Colfax, NC 27235
Phone: 336-996-8653
Fax: 336-996-8445
www.wayneleupold.com

Westminster John Knox Press
See Presbyterian Publishing Corporation

Word Music Group, LLC
20 Music Square East
Nashville, TN 37203
Phone: 615-733-1880
Fax: 615-733-1885

Meter Index

Tune Name Index

Index Of Authors, Composers, And Sources

Index of First Lines and Common Titles

Additional indexes and information on some
of the songs included in this collection can be
found at www.hymnary.org.